OPEN UP

This really happened.

*If present, past, and future break apart and bleed into one
as you read, consider that the light around you is sourced
from your present, reflected off the mirror of your past,
and bent through the lens of your future.*

*Where you are, where you've been, and where you want to be,
all influence what you see right now.*

Two loves I have of comfort and despair,
Which like two spirits do suggest me still:
The better angel is a man right fair,
The worser spirit a woman colour'd ill.
To win me soon to hell, my female evil
Tempteth my better angel from my side
And would corrupt my saint to be a devil,
Wooing his purity with her foul pride.
And whether that my angel be turnd fiend
Suspect I may, yet not directly tell;
But being both from me, both to each friend,
I guess one angel in another's hell.
Yet this shall I ne'er know, but live in doubt,
Till my bad angel fire my good one out.

William Shakespeare, Sonnet 144

HELLO

Bill seems a little down on the opposite sex. After likening his internal 'worser spirit' to a woman, he trumpets an arguably sexist metaphor, his Shakespearean plea bearing fruit ripe for cancel culture picking.

Perpetually-offended America was a century from a zygote in 1599, when he wrote this first-recorded reference to a 'better angel.' And while I do believe a better angel is at work inside me, I don't consider her opposite to be a 'female evil.' I'd call that other, less virtuous voice my 'bitter angel,' who's caustic frustration with the outside world generally emanates from some misdirected inner truth.

My earliest misdirected inner truth emanated from my urethra in the summer of my eleventh year, just as my dad propped himself onto his elbows and leaned his back against the headboard.

What are you doing?

The *what* was obvious, but I wasn't sure of the *why*, and the neglected drool tracing down my chin offered no clues. I knew I'd walked down the hall this mid-June night, lifted the lid on the dirty clothes hamper at the foot of my parents' bed, and was currently swaying in place, peeing all over their undies and pantsuits.

Rendered mute, yet aware of the order of things, I closed the lid, headed into their bathroom to wash my hands, and shuffled back down the hall to my room.

I'd just crawled into bed when a deep dad-shadow growl, more observation than question, startled me into responsiveness.

What the hell was that.

Shamed, embarrassed, and confident that this peeing misadventure had irreparably negated any chance of getting a surfboard for my upcoming eleventh birthday, I hauled my parents' soaked clothes downstairs to the washing machine, before defending in vain the brown shag carpet against the urine that had already soaked through the hamper.

My interrogation continued at breakfast, under the harsh exposure of the dinette light, where I could only describe stilted, undefined scenes: the creaking hinges of the hamper's vinyl lid, the hiss of piss on polyester, perhaps a dribble on my Star Wars pajamas.

My dad found the answer echoing through the ceramic bowels of his coffee cup, a single-word explanation which, had my almost-eleven-year-old compass been adjusted for metaphor, might have helped me avoid more self-destructive hampers down the road.

Sleepwalking.

That road would climb uphill in the darker hours and ease downhill during the day, when I'd often be unaware of the brilliant cobalt sky, or the wildflowers springing from the shoulder, because my bitter angel's leftover night-vision was still trained on the cracks in the asphalt.

This book's slightly raucous, unruly fraternal twin, *Living Halfway*, told my life-in-a-day story through that bitter angel's eyes, as I navigated the loss of my mom, as I knew her, to dementia. I didn't focus my lens as tightly on her journey in those pages, but the frustrated social commentary woven through the tale was as much a mirror to my own grief as, dare I say, an ode to what many of us think about our comparative culture, but rarely express.

Ghosts from the past drifted down my hallway that day, as my bitter angel wrestled with the realization he'd been living halfway to *someday*.

And while that narrative was true, my better angel was there, too.

This is his story.

HALO

I'm a million miles away, floating along the western edge of the nature preserve down the street from my house, where the dawn mist clings to the willows and a soft sea wind blows dove melodies from the cottonwood trees.

I touch down in an off-trail patch of clay loam, between scrub oak and chaparral, then again, and again, as I stealthily avoid a guy in a gray t-shirt brushing the waist-high grass with his fingers, a denim-clad bearded hipster on his phone, and an Instagram darling taking golden-hour selfies by the grand eucalyptus.

I grieve best alone and in motion, as if I can escape this creeping pathos born in losses manageable when singular, but quietly consuming when compounded, each step hitting the anticipated backbeat of a verse born when I was still writing songs.

The whole time I was running
I thought I was running away
From the ghosts in my corridor
Of loves lost along the way

The bordering band of cottonwoods births me onto a small peninsula overlooking a tidal flat, the same crop of land where I saluted a big brown dog in the wind, the day I had to let her go. I slow to a walk, then stand at the edge, heart turned toward the sliver of ocean visible to the west.

A rustle in the reeds below hints at a coyote, or a heron, or maybe a mountain lion looking for easy prey, but two huge ears affirm this is none of those.

To witness a deer this close to the sea is to take a step back in time, when the sprawl of this coastal county was mostly riparian wetlands. These thousand acres of nature preserve are themselves an ancient testament, having escaped the claws of planned community developers who never seem to live in the communities they develop.

The deer takes a step into the water and starts swimming toward a small island a few hundred feet away. Another creeps out of the reeds, and another, until a dozen of them are moving single file across the hydric channel, silent wakes stretching into the horizon.

A gangly youngster is struggling to keep up. I follow her eventually successful dog-paddle until she joins the herd on dry land, where she shakes with the same full-bodied hop perfected by that big brown dog now in the wind, who drops her halo into the early light refracting through the mist.

And I am absorbed into an unexpected presence, transfixed by how the most beautiful moments can't be timed, or planned, or manipulated, how the most beautiful moments can't be captured looking through a screen, because when we capture through a screen, we miss capturing through our heart.

Another gust of that big brown dog challenges me to a contest.

And I race her brilliant, raging sunrise, all the way home.

LOST

Clouds cling to early morning paint, fighting the color's release to the cobalt sky, as I stare out the window at the river bottom that doubles as my front yard. My toes grip the small woolen rug I found buried in the basement of a local furniture store last week: three woven Labradors sitting in a canoe, black at one end, brown in the middle, yellow at the other. The black and brown dogs face the same direction, which seems to be away, but the smaller, yellow one looks forward.

The universe didn't fabricate this rug for me, nor did I commission a particular weaver to latch-hook my two dogs in the hued sequence they appeared in my life, as masters of majestic canine destiny perched in a canoe. Except the yellow one. I don't know what that's about.

But as I laid this woven tarot on the kitchen floor in front of the sink, I did wonder how many other rugs, paintings, books, songs, haikus, or whatever, might be out there, waiting to be discovered, made for anyone, yet only for me.

I turn my waiting cup in a half-circle on the kitchen counter, my still-sweaty index finger hooked through the handle. I thought I might marry the girl who gave me this mug, emblazoned with a photo of my dog and *Love You To The Moon And Back* on the blue ceramic.

She's not dropping halos from heaven with the big brown dog, though.

She's living 15 minutes away in one of those hip tiny houses built on a flatbed trailer, and apparently seeing someone, which she hurriedly wedged into a conversation about something else entirely last month.

I didn't bother stopping her mid-sentence, asking her to rewind back to the casual mention and demanding details. I've seen the pattern before. What good would knowing do, when the end stays the same?

The coffeemaker proudly sounds completion in harmony with a hum of metal and glass vibrating from the counter, where my phone shows a blocked number. I let the call go to voicemail, but after a breath, the buzzing insistently resumes. This could have something to do with my mom, like the hospital or a concerned neighbor calling, so I answer with a hesitant hello.

You hear one with bird?

Huh?

One with bird, you hear it?

13

Who is this?

Look for text.

The line goes dead and, of course, I do what the heavily-accented voice told me to do.

I look for a text.

Nothing.

Whatever.

The only reason I answered was because a couple of weeks ago, a neighbor found my mom wandering around in the freezing mountain night, wearing only her nightgown and socks.

Lost.

SUNSHINE

I fill the ceramic mug with liquid aroma and take tiny sips as I get a box of granola from the pantry, yogurt from the fridge, and blueberries from the freezer. I've been attempting to perfect this breakfast concoction ever since I wandered into a Manhattan bistro last summer, in the middle of an east coast tour spent performing songs to apprehensive audiences of three to four people, including bar staff.

The attentive server patiently guided me through the difficult-to-pronounce menu options, but his energy shifted when he described the homemade-granola-local-yogurt-fresh-blueberry bowl, emphasizing that the yogurt was *fresh as the sunshine*.

I asked if the granola had raisins, because I'd had a traumatic childhood experience not only with the word *sunshine*, but also prunes, and considered raisins to be their smaller cousins.

When I was seven, a wave of confusion carried me into the second call-back for my first-ever commercial audition. My aunt knew a child agent, and I was an acceptably cute towhead who could remember my lines in the mandatory church Christmas plays, so my mom had asked if I wanted to try being on TV.

She'd refused to tell me exactly what product this commercial was advertising, and I found out why a few minutes later, when the casting director handed me a soft squishy orb much larger than an awful, dreaded raisin.

I was told to put this suspicious blob in my mouth, smile, and say *Tastes Like Sunshine*. As the unidentified foreign object passed under my nose, I caught a faint whiff of unfamiliar sweet pungency, triggering immediate guttural revulsion in every cell of my being.

Loosening my jaw and inhaling, I attempted to deliver *Tastes Like Sunshine*, only to re-taste my morning Cheerios on a strange mist sneaking up from my tummy. A small office trash can appeared in front of me on my exhale, and as I bent to rest my forehead against the plastic edge, shame, apprehension, and anxiety gave the prune an unnecessary final push.

Ensuring an appropriate projectile path, I noticed the liner was already almost full of barely chewed soft squishy orbs. Relief and gratitude for not being alone easily eclipsed my slight pause at these gastric iterations, which were far worse than their inspiration.

Over the next couple of years, I continued to expel many products I was supposed to sell, like Coca-Cola, which raked bubbly fake syrup across my no-sugar-allowed-at-home palate, and instead of falling gloriously down my throat, went shooting out of my nose in tiny inverse geysers. I also returned a spoonful of Cool Whip to the sender, and spit up a decidedly non-Maple-and-Brown-Sugar varietal of Quaker Instant Oatmeal all over Wilford Brimley's lap.

My two front teeth fell out during a Heath Bar commercial, but not because I didn't like chocolate. I didn't know there was an unreasonably hard substance called *toffee* in the middle of the candy bar, which was plenty resistant to push out my already jiggling incisors after a single enthusiastic bite. No longer the ideal spokesboy for a candy bar company, they sent me to an emergency dentist down the street, who made a contraption that looked like the retainer my sister had to wear after she got her braces off, except with two little white nubs that fit where my baby teeth used to be. Every time the director told me to bite down and smile, I'd wince from the searing pain of plastic and porcelain digging into my freshly abandoned gums, which wasn't a good look, either.

Expulsion wasn't limited to the oral cavity. I also peed the bed on a movie set, with Farrah Fawcett, Sam Elliot, Andy Griffith, and Katherine Ross watching from behind the camera, in a scene where I was supposed to pretend I was asleep, but actually fell asleep.

Perhaps my greatest involuntary projectile encounter, however, involved a product I actually loved, more than anything else in the world. Besides Star Wars action figures, of course.

Skippy.

In a scene touched by the hand of God, I found myself sitting at a picnic table, in awestruck grandeur and actual sunshine, next to the super-hot former Mouseketeer Annette Funicello, having an adult conversation about hiking and lunch.

All while eating peanut butter on white bread sandwiches.

In retrospect, I think the assumption by all parties, except me, was that I'd take a single bite from the brand-new, perfectly-made sandwich that magically appeared in front of me before each take, say a line, chew, and answer when Annette asked me what I liked best about hiking. Which I did, before downing the whole sandwich every time the director yelled *Cut!*. I mean, this was Skippy on Wonder Bread.

Who wouldn't?

The fifth take began like the others. I did my part and listened to Annette explain about how delicious and nutritious Skippy peanut butter was. She asked me what I liked best about hiking, and I said *Lunch*.

She said *It's Hard to Beat Skippy*, and as she held up two jars of peanut butter, regular and old-fashioned, I gagged.

But quietly, because this was a good take.

And then a little louder, enough for Annette to notice.

She grabbed me by the shoulders, spun me off the bench, swept me into her arms, and carried me to her fancy trailer, where she opened the door and told me to run to the bathroom in the back.

The director's *That's the keeper! Print it! Lunch, everybody!* was the coda to the final scene of my prunes-to-peanut-butter television journey, which ended full-circle with the not-quite-child-star hacking up the product in the trailer of a real star, who sent me birthday cards every year until I was sixteen.

Because not long after, I decided to quit show business, and spend my after-school hours playing handball against the garage door in the alley, instead of sitting in the backseat of my mom's car on the four or five hour round trip to Burbank for auditions.

She'd leave work early at least a few days a week, always stopping at home to put a wet washcloth and my favorite Chicken in a Biskit crackers in a Ziplock bag, on her way to my elementary school. There'd be the slog through traffic on the 405 freeway, as she rehearsed my lines with me from the driver's seat and constantly managed the AC, so the car wouldn't overheat. She'd wait for me to audition, battle a worse slog home on the 405, and then get dinner on the table.

Those pieces of her are gone now. She can't use the stove anymore, and the last time I asked her to look in the refrigerator, she walked into the pantry. She hasn't driven since the afternoon she tried to study for the written driver's test, and threw down the manual in teary frustration, because reading each sentence took forever.

That's also why they call that freeway the '405,' you know.

It takes 4 o' 5 hours to get anywhere.

19

LITTLE EGG

I'm rinsing out the bowl in the sink when the phone screen lights up again, this time with a text.

Wenn etwas mir vom Fenster fällt
(und wenn es auch das Kleinste ware)
wie sturzt sich das Gesetz der Schwere
gewaltig wie ein Wind vom Meere
auf jeden Ball und jede Beere
und tragt sie in den Kern der Welt.

A blocked call follows right away, which I assume is from the same guy.

You get text?

Yeah, but I can't read it. Who is this? Did I forget to pay a bill?

I write German.

What about English?

My English writing not so good. Do your own... how do you say... interpretalation. Interweb is magic, no?

Why should I even care about this?

You answered phone, yes?

I suppose I did.

I skid the phone across the counter and glance aimlessly into the yard, my gaze resting on the makeshift bird shelter I built from an empty oil barrel and a few roof tiles, next to where my girl-friend's trailer used to be. She didn't live in the trailer, though. She lived here, with me, the first person I ever let into my space for longer than a handful of nights. Five years, gone.

Both she and her trailer were still around last month when I found a little egg resting on the pavers near the front door. The egg must have fallen from somewhere, but a cursory search re-vealed neither nook nor nest, only a remarkable survival for such a delicate shell.

I knew some sort of bird haven was hidden under the trailer, because I'd watched a mama finch toting pieces of lint, grass, and tiny branches into a space in the aluminum frame.

Maybe she'd be open to adoption.

I cradled the little egg in my palm, shuffled down to the yard, and ducked under the metal sheathing. Four scraggly heads un-expectedly popped up, tiny beaks squawking, which made me squawk in retaliation and drop the little egg.

I wish I could say that the shell broke, and a beautiful bird emerged in sweet release, taking majestic flight into the blue skies of forever. But the shell broke, and yolk splattered all over the gravel. Not all over, I guess. This egg was little.

I felt like I'd irreparably disrupted the circle of life, and as penance, assumed the role of protector for the surviving chicks. Their nest was so well-placed, wedged high between an upper beam and solid metal, that nothing bigger than the mama bird stood a chance at infiltration.

Undeterred by my expendability, I took my mission seriously. The initial threat came later that afternoon, from a hawk perched on the fence a long way from the nest, head cocked in investigation of a lizard sunning himself on the gravel. I bravely pelted the potential offender with rocks, until he retreated to the top of the pepper tree.

I mounted several similar defenses over the next couple of weeks, while watching the chicks grow more fuzz, then feathers, testing their wings until my daily bird check-in revealed an empty nest.

Empty, but for a brand new egg already nestled in the shell remnants, in place of the little egg that never was. The next morning, another egg appeared. Then another. And another. And two more.

I hadn't disrupted the circle of life as irreparably as I thought.

But I got another chance, since both trailer and owner were set to move away yesterday afternoon. The nest wouldn't have survived hookup and hauling, so I dragged a barrel next to the trailer and set up a small, covered platform with some pavers and a few curved roof tiles.

Using a spatula and a towel, I lifted the nest from the aluminum underside to the makeshift shelter, hoping the mama bird would somehow find her unhatched young. And I would somehow find new purpose, in this protection of the displaced, as the shared life I knew pulled away.

Which is why I'm watching the makeshift shelter now for signs of maternal activity, balls of my feet dug into the Labrador rug. Poking around the nest isn't going to encourage the mama bird to come back, so I postpone my in-person evaluation and turn my attention to the welcoming worn cushions of the couch.

I doom-scroll through my phone for a few minutes, searching for distraction in the click-bait misery of digital news. I find what I'm looking for, with the added bonus of induced sour disposition, and show myself a little mercy by shifting gears into investigative reporting.

My search for a German translator tool yields a pile of options promising to be the best. Unsurprisingly, the Google translator sits at the top of the pile. I'll go with what's behind door number free, and probably get what I pay for.

I copy and paste what the mystery messenger sent me, hit return, and get back

When something falls from the window
(even if it were the smallest)
how the law of gravity overturns itself
mighty as a wind from the sea
on every ball and every berry
and carries them to the core of the world.

Almost makes sense, kind of.

The guy said to use interpretalation, which I'm interpreting as interpretation, and the best way I know to interpret anything is by writing lyrics. I haven't written a song in a long time, but I could try turning this slightly confused jumble of words into a poem, which is really just a song without a soundtrack.

My notebook is back in the bedroom, so I head down the hall, sit on the tangle of sheets, and flip to a blank page. I write and read and rewrite until I have

When even the smallest thing has fallen
Gravity takes hold
Strong as a gale deep through the ocean
Into the world's fold

Familiarity tugs from *the smallest thing has fallen*.

The little egg.

And me.

My memory of being small favors a lot more falling than standing.

Usually by accident, except for when I faked a fall on the 4th of July.

ELEVEN

Seeking absolution from the previous month's sleep-peeing debacle, I'd almost eclipsed my *Pitfall* high score on the Intellivision
when my mom yelled up the stairs. We were leaving early for the
4th of July festivities at the local golf course, so I could partake
in the pre-fireworks gladiator games, where my parents hoped I
would meet a new best friend. Even a marginal friend would do,
really.

I loved reading about the American Revolution, imagining myself
an integral part of secret meetings in dark corners of low-ceilinged
taverns. But I'd never been a fan of Independence Day at the golf
course. While the sight of make-believe bombs bursting in air
didn't really bother me, I hated the punishing blasts of vibration
and gunfire delivered a breath later. Those aggressive, deeply reso-
nant punches to my gut made me cry when I was a little kid, even
when my mom covered my ears with cupped hands.

But I had just turned eleven. Good conscience and reputation
wouldn't allow such coddling. I'd have to fight through the assault this year like a man.

A boy even smaller than me approached the moment I walked into the event amphitheater between the well-trodden putting green and divot-ridden 1st fairway. My monolingual inability to decipher his intent necessitated a deal brokered by his dad, who told me his son was a very fast runner, but didn't have many friends, so would I consider a proposition?

I agreed to having my left leg tied with burlap strips to his son's right leg, leaving me without my own leg to stand on, and requiring coordination across ethnic, linguistic, and cultural lines to even complete the three-legged race, let alone ensure victory.

I was intrigued by the kid's competitive vibe, as well as the promise of his speed, which meant I might finally have a shot at some semblance of actual victory.

We lined up with the other kids and waited for the whistle to blow, gesticulating last-minute plans for domination with our eyes and hands. We'd start with the middle leg, then our outside legs, until we found our groove, at which point we'd take off like a three-winged bat out of hell.

The whistle blew and we stayed true. We'd underestimated the brilliance of our plan, because all but two other teams tumbled to the fescue in their first steps. My cohort whispered *Uno Dos Tres*, which I understood from an early Sesame Street episode, and we took off, indeed, like a three-winged bat out of hell.

A lot went through my mind in those final twenty yards. Maybe this is what Phil Mahre was feeling in the poster on my wall, en route to winning Olympic gold in skiing. Maybe I really could be friends with this kid. Maybe I was going to finally win one. And if I was going to win one, I was going to win one in dramatic fashion. Lucky observers would be talking about my heroic final effort for the rest of their lives, and the humiliation that had followed me these twenty days since the sleepwalking incident would be erased forever.

Only one other team still survived, and they were falling behind in my peripheral vision. Convinced of victory, I knew that collapsing across the finish line would be the best scene to indelibly burn into spectators' memories, even if there was no need to actually collapse.

I'd seen enough World Cup matches with flopping Brazilians to know the drill.

And so, a torso-length away from the finish line, I tripped over nothing at all.

My forehead dug into the soft earth, a sure badge of honor I'd offer when taking the obligatory post-race victory photos. I looked up just as the other team rambled past us, shouting with surprised joy. My new-no-longer-friend looked at me with angry confusion, as if I'd microwaved a puppy.

I might as well have. I'd dragged us down a couple of feet short of the finish line.

Our dads rushed over and helped us to our feet, which was proving impossible to accomplish on our own, given our tangle of bound legs. I reluctantly accepted my second-place plastic trophy, which was essentially the last-place plastic trophy, since no other teams crossed the finish line, and trudged over to my waiting mom on the blanket.

The fireworks had just started when my dad offered another observation hinting at question.

You made yourself fall.

The bombs started bursting in air.

And my mom didn't try to cover my ears.

The back of my bare thighs stuck to the K5's vinyl backseat on the drive home, humidity blanketing the night as heavy as the shame over my pride. My dad parked in front of the house, since the garage was newly occupied by my sister's poop-brown two-door Audi Fox with a cassette player. She'd somehow passed her driver's test six months earlier, and with her summer hostessing job and a little help from my parents, now possessed the keys to the universe. I knew there was some sort of magic within that tin can, because she seemed to always come out happier than when she went in.

Freedom was not something I'd considered as a reason.

As soon as the family settled in to watch *Knight Rider*, I slipped into the garage and climbed behind the wheel of the Fox. The keys were in the ignition, and while I couldn't reach the pedals, I thought maybe if I turned the car on, magic would ensue, and my foul outlook on the rest of my life would improve.

29

Magic did ensue, and would, for the rest of my life.

Because blasting through the speakers at an unreasonable volume was a reedy voice telling me that even the losers got lucky sometimes, a lyric refrain I'd hear again at random yet appropriate moments down the road, like the afternoon I found out I was accepted to zero colleges: detours seemingly devastating, but really just bends in the asphalt, leading to the same town.

I hit the clicker on the visor to open the garage door for ventilation, because I was going to be here for awhile, and didn't want to die anymore, although I never really did. The engine wasn't even running, but I'd seen a movie where somebody died in a garaged car, and didn't want to take any chances.

I hit rewind on the cassette player, and listened again from the top.

It was nearly summer/we sat under the roof

Except this already was summer, and this was the garage, and this guy might have sounded like he was singing through his nose, but for the first time, I could actually understand the words to a song, and connect them to me.

Even the losers get lucky sometimes
Even the losers got a little bit of pride

That first chorus hit the door speakers, which launched me into a frenzy. I threw my fists in the air, like I was on Space Mountain at Disneyland, knocking a random, unimportant stick to the right with my elbow. The car started moving backwards, and even if I'd known to hit the brake, I couldn't have reached the pedal.

And so, my sister's Audi Fox rode a slow momentum out of the garage and into the same wall I'd crashed eyes-closed on training wheels when I was five, albeit with a much more substantial crumpling of metal against concrete block.

My perceived punishment was day camp, sponsored by the local YMCA and free for all kids, especially the ones I hid from during the school year. My mom and dad worked full-time and refused to hire a babysitter to watch me rearrange the Star Wars action figures in my bedroom, so regardless of my non-driving debacle, I probably would've been forced to succumb to the cruelty of these last four weeks of manufactured pubescent socialization.

The finale climaxed in a wasted mid-August afternoon at the poorly maintained local waterpark, which I could have more safely approximated with a plastic tarp and garden hose on the cracked concrete sidewalk in front of my house. And while I didn't find a soulmate in the hyper-chlorinated atmosphere, I did discover that I was just as sensitive on my bottom as I was everywhere else.

I fumbled for the elusive fiberglass splinters embedded just below my butt cheeks as we lurched away from the tangle of slides and pools. Sunlight dulled against the smudged, repurposed school bus window, and I scrutinized the streaks in the glass, hoping this search would steer my attention away from David Bartoli's asthmatic victory lap.

He'd just French-kissed Tammy K. in a mysterious, unseen cavern at the back of the bus, and awash in newfound glory, was striding up and down the aisle telling us about the victory. Repeated demands for him to sit down were lost in boisterous claims of pre-pubescent manhood, propelled through the atmosphere on plumes of spittle, born in gooey chomps on doubled-up Bazooka bubble gum.

This sexual conquest banter inspired a perfect storm of repulsion, fear, and confusion, forcing me into the far reaches of the solo vinyl bench, where I resigned my final summer fate to pulling tiny glass shards out of my ass.

And stressing about Jessica.

David's kissing and telling shined an uncomfortable light on my own relationship status. A couple of weeks before 6th grade ended, David had cornered me by the lockers with the intel that Jessica Nystrom would be waiting by the tetherball court at recess for me to utter six era-defining words:

Will. You. Go. Around. With. Me.

David advised that she was eagerly anticipating my inquiry, so chances of rejection were slim. Also, these six words would cement our standing amongst a mildly interested peer group, which was considerably more important than my understanding of the particulars.

Still uncertain as to what obstacle we'd actually be going around, I dutifully approached the tetherball court after history class, sweat dripping from armpits unburdened by deodorant, and forced a *Will. You. Go. Around. With. Me.* on whatever small, tentative breath I could muster.

Jessica said *Yes*, which translated into my spending every waking moment of 6th grade's waning weeks trying to avoid her by the drinking fountains, in the hallways, and on the playground.

Staring now at my distorted reflection in the dirty school bus window, I was forced to acknowledge that, given my naive, un-informed belief that some sort of actual communication would be necessary for a breakup, I was technically still going around with Jessica Nystrom.

I suppose we've been together ever since.

I never talked to her again.

My dad's K5 Blazer was idling in the YMCA parking lot when we pulled in. He'd gotten off work early to drive me to Hun-tington Beach, where, despite the sleepwalking debacle and my horrid 4th of July performance, a birthday blue G&S thruster was awaiting selection on the used surfboard rack.

We walked to the beach straight from the surf shop, my tiny hands keeping the board balanced on my head. My dad said he couldn't get his first board under his arm, either, and that I should just ignore the other kids making the trek around us.

That was his only advice for my first time trying to surf. He watched from the sand as I struggled to get to my knees, in between relentless shore-break beatings. My matchstick arms gave out in short order, and I rode in on my belly, dejected and embarrassed. I rolled off the board and onto the sand, where my dad was waiting with an offsetting, yet harmonious observation to June's confused *You made yourself fall.*

You didn't stand up.

I had nothing against the kneeboarders and bodyboarders out there, flying past me on their yellow Mach 7s with the slick black bottoms.

But my dad surfed.

And I was eleven now.

Eleven, saltwater burning eyes, blood rushing through small veins.

Eleven, unable to articulate the hollow uncertainty I found between leaving the safety of my knees and standing on my own two feet, too young to diagnose the risk festering in that purgatory, under the watchful eyes of my dad, with my own fragile confidence hanging in the balance.

Eleven, time to stand up.

YESTERDAY

Eleven.

Something was happening at 11:00.

Claire.

I'm supposed to meet her on the northern edge of the county. Her Labrador had a litter of puppies, and I've been thinking about getting another dog.

I'll have to race to get to her place in time, so I dump the last of my coffee, gone cold from staring out the kitchen window into my 11th summer, hustle to the garage, and climb into my truck, where Guns 'n Roses *Use Your Illusion II* propels me up I-15 with sonic rocket fuel.

A half-hour later I'm sitting on the kitchen floor in a two-room cabin, on an acre of land nestled between strip malls and auto superstores. A couple of eight-week-old Labradors are tumbling over each other toward me, one a yellow female, the other a black male. The male puts his tiny paws on my left knee and cries with excitement, which I would have misconstrued twenty years ago as the song of two souls connecting. The female sniffs my shoe and licks the shin of my jeans, before laying down in front of the stove to watch the world unfold.

Claire tells me I have a few hours to decide. *Other people are interested, you know.* I peel myself off the linoleum as she takes the puppies back to their mom, watching from behind the wire fence that designates a corner of the kitchen as the puppy-safe zone.

Axl Rose is still belting from the truck speakers when I hit the onramp on the way home.

Yesterday's got nothin' for me
Old pictures that I'll always see
Time just fades the pages in my book of memories

I've got old pictures, too, in that chest under the bedroom window that I haven't opened up in years, time likely fading the pages.

Those yesterdays have almost too much for me, though... the weight of what used to be is even heavier, now that my mom's yesterdays weigh nothing.

Her short-term memory has fallen off a cliff since that morning last summer when she said she recognized the hills and water and sky. We'd just pulled into a dirt parking lot near their house in the mountains, and I thought maybe the door to the increasingly unpredictable dark tower elevator had opened onto a familiar floor, and this would be a better day.

More like normal.

We carried our fly fishing rods down to the spring creek, and I waded off the near bank, while she followed my dad a couple hundred yards upstream. Her encouraging platitudes as he casted his line drifted relief around my bare calves. Finally, he was able to do something fun, something he'd earned, without her demanding to be anywhere other than wherever they were.

After fewer caught fish than strikes, I saw her walking the trail back up to the truck. I yelled and waved. She strained to shout that she was just going to sit down, and she'd see me soon.

She sounded happy.

But things had started to go south when she was left alone, so I brought in my line, trudged out of the creek, and fast-walked up the trail after her. My dad was already ahead of me, trying to catch her before she got to the truck. As I approached the open passenger door, she sputtered in anger that she was hot and didn't want to talk to me anymore.

My dad hit the brakes on a bridge linking the dirt road to the two-lane highway, and asked her if she wanted to see the bigger fish congregating in the shadows below. She whispered *I don't want to* in between sobs, the toddler intonation reminding me of the year before, when we were caught in a rainstorm and all she could say was *I'm so cold.*

I watched her in the side mirror as the truck cut home through the high-desert alpine prairie. She fought and lost to waves of tears, her mouth turned downward in sadness, or anger, or something else entirely. Maybe she was thinking about what was happening to her now, or what happened to her as a kid in foster care.

I didn't really know. I never do. She doesn't talk when she's crying, but when they dropped me off on their way to a doctor's appointment, I opened the passenger door, asked what was wrong, and brushed away the lone tear running down her cheek.

She shook her head.

Nothing to do with you.

Which wasn't true, of course.

Everything about this has something to do with me.

I shut her door, stepped back on the gravel driveway, and watched the truck disappear into the dust.

The truck, and another piece of her.

Maybe I'll get one of those puppies. That little yellow one was kind of like the girl sitting alone at the bar who doesn't know she's beautiful, which is why she has no problem sitting alone at the bar.

HER

I stop by Trader Joe's for supplies and snacks in the middle of the lunch-time rush. I have to fly out later today to play a show half-way across the country, and nothing says plane fare like whatever these peanut butter-filled pretzel things are called.

Two women are having a chat across the registers ahead of me, and they clearly have a lot of catching up to do, because the cashier can't get their attention.

Ma'am.

MA'AM.

You can pay now.

He comes around the counter, stands in between them, and says *MA'AM* again, a little louder, with enough hint of annoyance to make the rest of us smile.

No big deal, really. These ladies will be gone into the rest of their lives soon enough, and I'm not in a rush. My flight's not until later this afternoon.

So I'm not sure why my breath quickens, my forehead collapses in confused frustration, and my chin drops to my chest, as the muscles in my forearm tense and quiver, tense and quiver, and I don't know what's happening, but there are two of me in here, because this is his breath quickening, his forehead collapsing, his chin dropping to his chest, the muscles in his forearm tensing and quivering, tensing and quivering, until my body releases into a guy wearing a gray t-shirt a lot like mine, standing in front of me in line.

He turns sideways in consternation, mouth turned down, and impatiently shifts his weight from one foot to the other before closing his eyes, lost in an upper body sway, an actor in a story only he knows, as if he's taking in these women's conversation and morphing the dialogue into an anxiety-ridden internal saga. He looks familiar. I study the deepening lines on his face while the cashier breaks up the social hour, until he turns his back to me, stepping forward to dump his bachelor haul of granola bars and cereal onto the conveyor belt.

A few minutes later, I've loaded my bags into the backseat of the truck, and embarked on the epic journey of delivering the cart back to the pipe-framed corral at the opposite end of the lot.

Apparently, I'm the only one, because there are plastic-metal horses scattered everywhere across the asphalt, abandoned by weary warriors too consumed with the demands of battle to tend their steeds.

41

I've just added the seventh cart to this unwieldy train when I see her, returning her own empty cart just ahead of me.

Legs, scraped and skinned with living, anchored in cut-off jean shorts.

Small feet barely gripping grit-ridden flip-flops.

Silver hoop earring against tan cheek.

Long blonde hair falling from a frayed Seattle Mariners baseball hat, falling, falling, falling into the folds of lyric carbon paper copy memory.

And I will remember your long blonde hair
Falling all around me
One perfect moment when the world stopped and stared
At me tangled in you
And your long blonde hair

Hi.

Her?

No.

Her was the one.

And I'm standing at the Central Saloon in Seattle's Pioneer Square, after my first-ever band played our opening set, when *her* touches me on the shoulder, and I turn to find my next Jenny

Cooper, who was the truest love I'd known from a tween until then.

Her tucks her long blond hair behind her left ear and says *Your guitar player tells me you were on The Love Boat.* She notices then buys my favorite beer, and takes me back to her table, where I write my phone number down on the cover of one of the many CDs I don't sell.

Her is shuddering against me the next year as "No One Is To Blame" plays on the stereo in my cramped Seattle living room. We are destined to be together, forever, someday, as soon as she finds the self-worth to leave her abusive boyfriend and I find the self-worth to reclaim my always-available shoulder. And in the lonesome afterglow, when my empty reality catches the gray settling over the Space Needle, someone is, must be, to blame.

Her.

Her sits on the striped fabric couch in my tiny living room two years later, listening then crying, as I pick the first few notes of a song I've written about us. She's in another relationship now, one that she says makes her feel better about herself, because she's not ready to give me all that she knows she's capable of giving.

So I can't ask her to dinner, or a movie, or a drink, but I can write this song, I can walk around the area rug, guitar strap slung over my shoulder, and sing the first line about how I don't look at her when I talk to her.

43

And I don't look at her when I sing to her, either. I look through the window overlooking the skyline, I look through the back door to the yard, I look through my heart when I sing to her, about how we revolve around each other, planets held by the same gravitational force, dependent on each other, yet destined to remain a certain distance apart forever.

HI?!

I offer an apologetic *Hi* and ask if she wants me to return her cart, averting my gaze as our eyes meet.

She laughs and tells me I already have my hands full, before pulling a couple of carts from the end of my train. I fall in behind as she pushes them to the pipe corral, convinced I've finally found my soulmate, this beautiful girl who has anticipated a need and sacrificed to lessen my load, even though the offering is minor, and the time invested short.

The girl in the Mariners hat rides the cart-train like a skateboard, pushing off the asphalt with one foot while anchoring the other against the metal frame. She lets the carts float into the corral and turns to me with a hesitant hint of expectancy, before waving a goodbye and dancing away.

I exhale and breathe in that night at the same Central Saloon in Seattle's Pioneer Square, three years, countless slow-dances in the cramped living room, and songs written for *her* later, before my band plays another opening set, when I'm at the bar pay phone, checking my answering machine to see if *her* has left a message that she'll show up this time, but knowing she won't, because she

44

never has, not really, not like I'd dreamed she would, not like I sometimes still dream she will.

Do you remember a game of truth or dare
Playing out on the porch swing
We ran around in circles going nowhere
Just tangled in you
And your long blonde hair

My love I still go there
And dream under deep blue desert skies
Somewhere I'm lost in the soft summer air
With you and your long blonde hair

I shove the carts into the corral, the grinding clatter of empty disappointment drowning the wary confidence I'd considered mustering to say something else to the girl in the Mariners hat.

Doesn't matter. *Her* has already shown me how these things end, anyway.

There she goes, the Mariners hat already climbing into a red 4Runner, with a black Labrador poking his head through the lowered rear window.

Already backing out of the parking space.

Already giving me another little wave as she drives by.

Already gone.

As am I, lost in how a ghost from my past could still knock me down in this parking lot. I rest my head against the steering wheel and close my eyes against the soft vibration of the idling truck, buoying my dad's simple answer to the moot, rhetorical question.

You didn't stand up.

I did when I was twelve, though.

TWELVE

Love lift us up where we belong
Where the eagles cry
On a mountain high

An Officer and a Gentleman was on its millionth viewing in the den, courtesy of the marriage between our new VCR player's re-wind button and my sister's trigger index finger. I'd watched the movie with her once, and that was enough, since Richard Gere was not Luke Skywalker and Debra Winger was not Princess Leia.

And while my sister may have been the only family member camped out in front of the TV, the maxed-out volume left the rest of us no choice but to hear Joe Cocker and Jennifer Warnes making lyrical love on the VHS tape, over and over and over.

Love lift us up where we belong
Far from the world below
Up where the clear winds blow

I was already far from the world below.

Upstairs, in my room, legs crossed on the brown shag carpet.

Not yet ready to fully embrace the freedom of early summer life without the grounding element of homework, I was intent on drowning out Jennifer and Joe with the Davy Crockett *Indian Fighter* story album I'd just put on my tiny toy turntable.

I'd blinked in acceptance on my twelfth birthday a few weeks before, when I dutifully unwrapped this mostly plastic Fisher-Price record player. I was listening to Davy Crockett records, and didn't need a Realistic hi-fi to know that Chief Redstick and his tribe were causing big problems for the white man, making war to defend their land, and the United States Army needed Davy's help in finding them.

The instrumental version of "Up Where We Belong" downstairs poked through the breaths in the Davy Crockett story, and I knew what that meant.

The final, glorious, boy-gets-girl scene.

I closed my eyes and saw Richard find Debra in the factory and kiss her. I watched the freshly minted officer and now gentleman sweep the girl into his arms, carrying her past the machinery and into the rest of their lives, the frame freezing as she playfully transferred his hat to her own head.

I heaved an exasperated sigh, oblivious to the fact that Richard Gere had just imprinted a story I'd find impossible to replicate, and however eye-rolling I thought the song might be, in truth, I believed love would finally lift me up where I belonged, into a cottonwood sunset sky three decades later.

These stories that we hear and see and tell, that run like a current under our consciousness, alter our internal tides.

Whatever.

I wasn't even in eighth grade yet.

July brought more humid days than usual, and I spent the first morning begging my sister for a ride to the beach in her Audi Fox, so I could work on my surfing. My mom had acquiesced to letting me stay home from day camp this year, since my sister could keep an occasional eye on me, under the condition that I wouldn't turn anything on, besides the TV, and especially not the stove.

My sister conveniently remembered her baby oil for maximum tanning and her lemons to further blonde her hair, and her friends, but forgot her brother on her way to the beach. No lunch made for me, bored of cereal and banned from the toaster oven, I perused the dog biscuits in the pantry, partly out of curiosity, but mostly out of hunger.

They sure looked good.

My gag-reflex had been well-honed, born the afternoon I overheard my parents talking about needing to save money. Committed to doing my part as a four-year-old to help the family, I swallowed the spare change that my dad kept in a small wooden box on their bedroom TV, and promptly purged the Skippy peanut butter sandwich I'd had for lunch, quarters and nickels embedded in the Wonder Bread.

Saving money, I learned, was difficult.

I took a test nibble of the dog biscuit and lost what was left of my morning Cheerios, which helped inform my determination that opening a can of tuna didn't count as turning anything on. I torqued the rusty can opener in a stubborn circle along the rim, but didn't have the strength to get all the way around. Prying the lid open with my fingers led to slashing a gouge across my thumb, which spawned a continuous geyser of blood, immune to an entire roll of Brawny paper towels.

I'd never been left alone before, and if I was ever to be trusted again, my mom couldn't find out. Somehow she found out about everything.

I winced through Donahue, Oprah, and Sally Jesse Raphael, sorting through ways to deflect the damage. I decided the best option was to hold my hand under the table at dinner, but didn't account for the impact having a limb lower than most of my body would incur. My sister brought this to my attention midway through the beef stroganoff, when she shrieked at the gathering pool of blood under my seat.

And so, with eight stitches in my thumb, wrapped with a soft cast extending over my wrist, I was stuck on dry land for the foreseeable future. Whenever my sister was at the beach, I'd eject the *An Officer and a Gentleman* videotape and insert a surf movie I'd found sitting on top of a trash can in the alley. I thought maybe I could glean some tips from the pros in the movie, which would translate to my own oceanic dominance.

I must have watched one particular sequence, filmed on a sun-drenched summer day at Malibu, dripping with perfect waves and obligatory bikini shots, over a hundred times.

But not because of the girls, whose language I didn't yet understand, and not because of the surfing, which I'd realized I'd never come close to emulating.

I didn't even really watch that one particular sequence.

I listened to the song accompanying the three-and-a-half minute sequence. The moving pictures were collateral necessity.

The band's name was suspiciously missing from the soundtrack credits, and I had little recourse for figuring out how to procure the track. Album buying was still well out of my wheelhouse, and 1985 knew no internet. So, I kept hitting rewind on the VCR player over and over, allowing the firing guitar riff and massive, soaring vocal to lift me higher and higher into rock heaven.

Because there, while the music played, I could do anything. Maybe even make this glorious sound myself, when that firing guitar riff would inspire my first attempt at approximating notes on my sister's nylon-strung guitar, the massive, soaring vocal my first wail, this glorious marriage my lesson that all a song needed was three simple chords and the truth.

These same three simple chords would propel the first song I would ever write, the week my friend Ben shot himself to death in his mom's bathroom as we pulled up to his house for carpool. I would carefully script the words during Mr. Oswald's history class on lined notebook paper, about a magical place behind the mountains and beneath the ocean where I could disappear, and call the song "Sanctuary."

Now that the overplayed videotape had started to warp the song into more of a warble, I struggled even harder to understand the one lyric that the singer was hitting with the most emphasis, the most passion, the most meaning, so much so that I knew I must believe, must live by what he was saying.

Inside her you'll find sanctuary

Being of innocent mind and undeveloped body, even if I'd been able to decipher those words, they wouldn't have made sense to me.

Not yet.

A couple weeks before the first bell of eighth grade signaled summer's goodbye, my dad offered a late August day trip to a famous surf break an hour south. I'd heard that the waves were directly in front of an equally famous nuclear reactor landmark resembling huge titties, so this was a win-win.

I invited a couple of neighborhood kids that could be life rafts in the upcoming uncertain seas of junior high, and we left the house pre-dawn in my dad's Blazer, picking up donuts before braving the hour-long migration south. My dad turned up the radio louder than my mom ever allowed, to a rock station she didn't allow either, and for the first time I realized that my dad was a different person than my mom.

Despite not being able to get my arm wet for the last six weeks, I thought I was surf-ready. I'd spent countless hours in the living room doing one-handed pushups to my feet, as the sanctuary song pulsed in the background. Just in case, I spent the drive pondering which excuses I'd use when asked why I wasn't actually standing up on the board. Maybe inherited tight hips, or how the ocean felt closer and the wave seemed bigger from that vantage point. Both convenient and true, but also both more excuse than reason.

We parked, and a flurry of wetsuits and wax later, we were paddling through the waist-high waves, overestimating their size and our potential to dominate mother nature. One of the neighborhood kids turned to catch a wave, and I craned my neck to measure his progress against mine.

He was standing up.

A smaller wave came through, and I paddled until the water took over, committed to not settling, not this time. Like an arthritic geriatric, clamoring out of his easy chair at the nursing home on his way to the john, I clumsily pushed to my knees, then one foot with a knee down, and then both feet.

The guy to my left fell as the wave broke. I heard a hoot of approval to my right and shot a quick glance to see the neighbor-hood kid, who'd just caught the bigger wave, pushing his board back out in waist-deep water.

And one glorious breath later, I was tossed like a rag into the washing machine of whitewater.

But I didn't care. I'd taken a stand, for myself, literally, finally, even if for only a second.

I got to relive that moment over and over.

Because somewhere buried in that chest under the window is the only photograph my dad took that day that mattered.

The ancient, abandoned family slide projector rumbles in my mind, in time with this vibrating steering wheel of my idling truck in the Trader Joe's parking lot.

Whirrrr. Click.

LAUREL CANYON

This same road home once carried a younger me toward a wide-open future, which morphed into a trudging present, as I spent my twenties and early thirties playing my songs in other people's towns for anybody who'd listen, and many who wouldn't. Strands of getting older began to weave their way through my lyrics, the fabric heavy with unrealized dreams and unmet expectations.

I thought that I'd be there by now
But this night is echoing loud
As I drive

Innocent hubris, to be so certain I knew this rockstar dream was best for me, when my true calling may still be more beautiful than anything I could ever dream.

A lilting melody lifts the corners of my mouth, away from the downturn of not standing up in the Trader Joe's parking lot, and into a wry smile.

I was so much older then, I'm younger than that now.

Bob Dylan.

I wrote him off as a freak when I was thirteen, after seeing him play a show on TV with thick white paint on his face, sweat carving through the pigment like a nervous clown at a mobster's birthday party. Thankfully, my puberty-provoked snap judgement wilted in the sunlight of his songs, like "My Back Pages": a recantation of his early political hubris in what he called 'finger-pointing songs,' and where *I was so much older then, I'm younger than that now* lives.

Approximate technical fumbling with my phone at the next stop-light doesn't yield the original, but does find a famous cover of "My Back Pages," which is cranking through the truck speakers by the time the signal turns green. The Byrds sang this version from their Laurel Canyon perch, Roger McGuinn's 12-string Rickenbacker guitar carrying lush harmonies through the idyllic enclave, where folk music met rock and roll and the quiet platitudes of poetry rode amplifiers into a vibrant new beginning.

My own Laurel Canyon would forever be that kind of beginning, a time of discovery and renewal, but never a *before*, because *before* demands that the beginning ends, to make space for what comes after. And what comes after is never as good as the beginning, only a bastardization, like in Laurel Canyon, where the artsy pioneers with their weed and love songs eventually gave way to the soulless cocaine scene of impostors.

Is the hour too late to create this idyllic oasis of beginnings, where the poet meets the electric guitar? Too late to knock on each other's doors with our own songs, to play into the night, laughter echoing through our own Laurel Canyons?

Or are we resigned to now traipse through our anonymous comment sections and climb our digital walls, reducing our world to reaction and malaise.

Impostors, indeed.

I was so much older then, I'm younger than that now

The refrain circles one more time as the song fades, just as I pull up to the crosswalk at the next four-way stop. A cyclist flies across the intersection without stopping, middle finger in the air, forcing the truck next to me to brake violently to avoid a bloody tangle of metal and spandex. With an audacity possible only because the multi-geared messenger knows he's an asshole, the half-gloved F-you floats by, pointed at the guy in the other lane.

This mildly aggressive assault in place of apology doesn't really bother me. The finger is pointed at the other guy, so I'm not taking this personally. And besides, I'm currently building a dream in my own Laurel Canyon.

I don't think the guy to my right is building a dream, though. His palm is poised over the steering wheel, ready to fire. But the horn doesn't sound, probably only because in the aftermath of the near-miss melee, a kid has started walking his bike through the crosswalk.

Which gives me a minute to truly see who's next to me.

My breath quickens, my forehead collapses in confused frustration, and my chin drops to my chest, as the muscles in my forearm tense and quiver, tense and quiver, and I don't know what's happening, but there are two of me in here, because this is his breath quickening, his forehead collapsing, his chin dropping to his chest, the muscles in his forearm tensing and quivering, tensing, and quivering, until my body releases into the guy in the gray t-shirt, sitting rigid in the driver seat, as if he believes that the universe is plotting against him, and the cyclist is the messenger.

The guy in the gray t-shirt, staring fiercely into nothing, as if his angry eyes are hiding their search for a release more lasting than a palm pressed against a steering wheel.

The guy in the gray t-shirt, swallowing a shortened breath, as if stale air will burn away that unshakeable feeling that he thought he'd be there by now, wherever *there* may be.

Exhaling in defeat, as if he needs something to look forward to.

I call Claire and tell her I'll take the little yellow puppy.

HOMEGROWN SON

I'm on a conference call right now.

Except he isn't. He's standing in the middle of the street just past the next intersection, laboring under four trash bags stuffed to stretched-plastic capacity. His streaked hoodie is pulled over a frayed hat, grimed shorts drooping to his calves.

Concerned and mildly alarmed, I'd pulled over as soon as I saw him, and had offered a tentative *Hey man* as I approached him. He'd abruptly turned to me with wide, suspicious eyes sunk into gaunt, clean-shaven cheeks, and informed me of his current work obligation.

I'm on a conference call right now.

There are a lot of people who can't make rent, working but still unable to afford housing, homeless but not destitute, and I can't say for sure what his situation is.

But something isn't right.

We exchange a few sentences in the middle of the street, his muttered responses nonsensical, but with a rhythm of intention, reminding me of a few conversations I've had with my mom lately. She knows what she wants to say, and the cadence of the sentence is right, but the words she chooses aren't.

I lose track of his mangled response to my last probing question, staring past him into this cruel common denominator, to realize that this is the first time I've looked at my mom's dementia as a disease, rather than a thief.

But there's also an unease surfacing in my belly that has nothing to do with my mom, born in uncertainty as to whether his intent might suddenly shift. Each moment teeters more unpredictably on a darkening fulcrum, his speech and body movements becoming more erratic, until he grabs me by the forearm and doesn't let go.

I pry his fingernails out of my skin, say we'll talk later, wait for a car to pass, and head back to the truck. He drops his trash bags and follows me to the sidewalk, thanking me profusely for all I'm doing, all I've done, all I'm going to do. Gratitude is the stream of consciousness he's chosen to swim in for now, and there's nothing threatening about gratitude.

Until there is.

His escalating physicality provokes another common denominator, as I shut him out with my truck door, echoing the same thud of helplessness I felt last summer after fly-fishing.

What can I do?

And what can I say to this increasingly agitated man, as his gesticulation accelerates into wider arm swings, his speech spiraling into frantic discord?

What can I say to my high school friend and college roommate, with whom I'd awkwardly patrolled fraternity parties freshman year after traveling together overseas? The gifted musician with whom I'd played songs, the natural athlete with whom I'd surfed? The housemate, with whom I'd shared a living space and barbecues and good, honest times, less than a mile from where he's standing?

I haven't seen him in well over a decade, real contact lost in the vapid impermanence of text messages and social media, until there was no connection at all.

People talk self-assuredly about not needing to nurture certain relationships, enjoying friendships that pick up right where they left off, after years spent in different orbits.

Sometimes that happens.

But not always.

Not as an earnest sun fights through the thin marine layer blanketing this beach town, where a homegrown son once walked as a curious toddler, then as a confident teenager and searching young adult, and now as a ghost in a streaked hoodie, hurrying back to the four trash bags stuffed to stretched-plastic capacity, waiting for him in the middle of the street.

RELIC

I pull into the garage, cycling through the what-ifs, should-haves, and could-haves that have accompanied my frustrated impotence all the way home. The circle is mercifully broken by a text from Claire saying we forgot to figure out a time to pick up the little yellow puppy.

I kill the engine, smile, and write that I'll get her as soon as I'm back from my trip this weekend, and then walk-run through the living room to the bedroom, where I open up the chest under the window for the first time since I moved into this house.

The leather puppy collar that belonged to my very first dog, and will belong to my very last one, is somewhere in here.

I dig for the collar, under photo albums, pajamas I wore on *The Love Boat*, and the pink childhood blanket I couldn't sleep without, until my excavation is slowed by an unhinged Polaroid of me, smiling under the gaudy gold-leaf-framed painting my grandma found at a garage sale.

These relics we carry across generations.

Some we intend, others we don't.

My mom's mom died in the throes of dementia at 102, in a small suburban house converted into a mini-facility for severe patients, where they were dressed in each other's clothes, since no one knew the difference anyway.

Her husband passed away in 1980. My dad tried to give his complicated mother-in-law a dog for companionship a few years later, but she called him after two days and told him to take it back. She was okay being alone, in that big house on the hill.

We lived close as the crow flies. And while I didn't have a crow, I did have a dog, the first one to wear the puppy collar, who knew every turn by heart and would pull me on my skateboard to her big blue front door.

A cavernous, magical otherworld waited inside. Her living room was dominated by an old, almost-discarded painting, which she'd found at a garage sale and bought for almost nothing because she liked the gold-leaf frame. Sleuthing by the local museum decades later discovered that the frame still held the centuries-old work of an Italian landscape master, and the painting had belonged to Napoleon.

Napoleon. Not Napoleon Dynamite. Napoleon.

That kind of magic was everywhere, from that painting to the talking mirror that grumbled whenever I walked past, which made the house feel full and alive, so I never thought of my grandma as alone.

Which is how I learned that alone doesn't have to mean empty.

She did things her way, per the Sinatra song, and had two sayings that you won't find in any holy scripture: *Money doesn't make you happy, but it sure as hell helps,* and *You come in alone and go out alone, no matter what happens in between.*

My grandma's doctor predicted imminent death several times during her last year, igniting a rush from wherever we were to a false alarm. She refused to quit, and had she been able to speak, would probably have attributed her strength to the Choctaw heritage and Okie blood she brought with her to Depression-era California.

She lived a story echoing through John Steinbeck's writings of a generation that learned to never, ever give up, because giving up meant dying; a generation that worked and saved as if their lives depended on it, because this was their truth; a generation that wasted nothing, because they had nothing; a generation we need now more than ever, but are losing, one by one.

She died in that small suburban house, with none of us around, just like she said she would.

My mom sat in the back seat on the way home from the funeral, holding roses, crying. She must have known what had just happened. Maybe she was thinking about her childhood, spent between foster care and a Masonic orphanage, leading to an entire life spent searching for her mother's approval and suffering intense emotional abuse along the way, even when her mother couldn't speak anymore.

Finally ending, but not, in that Long Beach mausoleum vault burial.

Or maybe she wasn't thinking at all.

I watched her in the rear-view mirror, staring out the window in what could have been confusion or apprehension or sadness or something she wouldn't talk about, like after we went fly fishing last summer.

Lost, in all she could and couldn't remember, having inherited a tragic relic.

As I may have, too.

Never eliminated, only countered in some subtle way, by another relic of magic and hope and possibility, like this small circle of worn leather, cracked and softened by firsts, tiny buckle fitted into tiny hole, draped over my fingers.

And the painting with the gold-leaf frame, now hanging on my own living room wall.

KARMA

They weren't all like Annette Funnicello.

Right here, under the pajamas, is the Snoopy autograph book that everyone I worked with as a little kid enthusiastically signed, except for three assholes. Two of them happened concurrently, on The Love Boat set, when Doc and Gopher didn't bother to turn around when I politely asked, once, and then again with louder hesitance, using Mr. and their last names, if I could please have their autograph. We'd just done a scene together, but they didn't even answer, only sauntered away somewhere else, maybe to lunch, or an unverified, unsubstantiated, slanderous early-80s cocaine break.

The other asshole is still in jail, I think.

He seemed so nice on TV. Funny, charming, happy around kids, and probably the biggest star of the era.

My mom had driven me at 5:30 that morning to be in a Jello Pudding Pops commercial with him. I'd been doing a lot of commercials that summer, despite the prune incident, mostly because I wasn't a head case, no assembly necessary, and came included with a non-stage mom. Word spread about that kind of anomaly.

And so we kicked a soccer ball back and forth after the director yelled *Action!* and I excitedly accepted the chocolate Jello Pudding Pop from his little cart, and said whatever I was supposed to say.

Only took one take.

I worked up the courage to approach him on his way to his trailer, buoyed by my mom's encouragement, since he'd smiled at me during our scene together. She said barely a minute had passed, and he'd remember me.

She took a picture on my approach, which was the only one he'd allow, and I offered the polite *Mr. last name* greeting and asked him if he'd please sign this Snoopy autograph book that my mom had bought at Thrifty.

He stopped, turned around, looked down, and said no.

That's all he said.

No.

He waved me away dismissively, stomped the few stairs up to the trailer, and disappeared into his aluminum castle.

You might wonder why I even bother to remember that story.

You might think that these small things don't matter, that there are bigger injustices in the world. You also might think that stiffing a seven-year-old didn't have anything to do with what happened down the road, when he was sent to prison for aggravated indecent assault, after more than sixty women came forward, post-statute of limitations, with charges of attempted sexual assault, drug-facilitated sexual assault, sexual battery, child sexual abuse, and sexual misconduct.

You might be wrong.

Being an asshole might've had everything to do with it.

PIECE OF HER

And now that I'm digging, I know there's a picture of my mom, laughing and alive, somewhere in this chest from those child-acting-but-really-just-memorizing days. I'd been on that same set where I peed the bed, and my make-believe brothers and I were supposed to splash around in the backyard pool, acting like we were cooling off on a hot August afternoon. This was a mid-December morning in Encino, and the empty rental house didn't have a pool heater, so our teeth were chattering as we hit a beach ball back and forth across the arctic, slightly green, chlorine-deprived waters.

The director mercifully took the first take, and I crawled out of the cold, with my OP trunks riding high against shivering stick legs. My mom wrapped me in the towel she'd thought ahead to bring, sat on the staged patio furniture, and held me against her until I stopped shaking.

Maybe this is what I still need, what we all need, to be held until we stop shaking, by a lover, or a friend, or a dog, or a mother, or a drug, or a song, whatever may calm the tremors left by immersion in reality's cold tonic.

And now, I'm pushed to my knees by the weight of this single found photograph, the grit of built-up dirt between the hardwood planks grinding into my skin as the tendons and protective tissue pinch between bone and grain. The sudden pain pushes tears to well, but not tears of sadness, born in remembering someone who can no longer remember me.

These are tears of unexpected anger.

Anger at what's happening to her. Anger at the heaviness that buries me in the past, because that's the only place I can still find her. Anger at my inability to build a bridge between the chasm separating me and these Polaroid versions of me. Anger at my anger, when I have so much to be grateful for.

I pinch my eyelids together tight to fight who can no longer be fought, watching the threads of gray cotton materialize into tactile registry behind my eyes. My breath quickens, my forehead collapses in confused frustration, and my chin drops to my chest, as the muscles in my forearm tense and quiver, tense and quiver, and I don't know what's happening, but there are two of me in here, because this is his angry breath quickening, his forehead collapsing, his chin dropping to his chest, the muscles in his forearm tensing and quivering, tensing and quivering, until my body releases into his and I grab a pillow from the bed and scream, scream, scream, scream into feathers and cloth, until we have nothing left to scream, and the linen is wet with exhausted rage.

71

Drained and tear-stained, I lay back on the bed with the photograph that brought me to my knees clutched to my chest, as if I hold the fragile paper to my heart and close my eyes, I will be in that moment again, in that slice of eternity that can't be taken away, because there is a piece of her in here, in me, that will never go anywhere at all.

ROOTS

I open my eyes and pull my head from the pillow, just as the phone lights up full-screen from the foot of the bed.

Ein jedes Ding ist uberwacht
von einer flugbereiten Gute
wie jeder Stein und jede Blute
und jedes kleine Kind bei Nacht.
Nur wir, in unsrer Hoffahrt, drangen
in einer Freiheit leeren Raum,
statt, klugen Kraften hingegeben,
uns aufzuheben wie ein Baum.
Statt in die weitesten Geleise
sich still und willig einzureihn
verknupft man sich auf manche Weise,
und wer sich ausschliebt jedem Kreise,
ist jetzt so namenlos allein.

The mystery messenger's timing was impeccable earlier, and a shift in gears is welcome, so I lean back against the headboard with my notebook and phone to take another swing at Goo-

73

gle-translator-interpretation. This one is even more awkward, and the best I can come up with is

Stone, blossom, and child
Have their place to belong
But we run reckless and wild
Away from where we are strong
To tangled knots of hurt
Struggles your's and mine
We must listen to the dirt
If we should rise like pines

But this is enough, this poetic mirror to a closed heart, wrapped in the paper mâché of the past, slowly turned against possibility and joy, not by a single catastrophe, but by seasons of quiet disappointment.

And I'm laying back in bed, in Laurel Canyon, walking a winding woodsy mountain road connecting the beehive of the Sunset Strip and the sprawling suburbs of the San Fernando Valley, the Byrd's harmonies and 12-string electric guitar floating through the trees from the peaceful heart of a metropolis. A bucolic beauty pulses through this California, a California I want to create, my own Laurel Canyon, where our house is a very, very fine house, with two cats in the yard. A very, very fine house, except the cats would be a dog and chickens and horses, and the yard would be a few acres in a river valley, where the calls of crickets and frogs keep the surface noise of city life at bay.

To everything (turn, turn, turn)
There is a season (turn, turn, turn)

And a time to every purpose under heaven

A time to be born, a time to die
A time to plant, a time to reap
A time to kill, a time to heal
A time to laugh, a time to weep

A time to listen to the dirt.

A time to rise like pines.

PERMISSION

I swing my feet to the floor and push off the mattress, my neglected stomach protesting as I stand up. I slide the piece of her in between the folds of a forgotten poetry book, not sure why the dog-eared paperback is in this chest. There's no inscription inside the front cover, just the title and poet's name.

Rainer Marie Rilke.

Maybe I kept this tome as a token from an unknowingly unrequited love, like Jenny Cooper's vanilla entry in my 8th grade yearbook, resting in a box in the garage, or the scribbled note from *Her* somewhere in this chest, saying my dog did fine after she pet-sat one weekend in the late '90s.

BT.

Before texting, and a lot of things that make life more convenient and less mysterious, including the formerly-building-sized computer connected to the world and living in my pocket, next to the puppy collar.

Sometimes I wonder if this phone is serving me, or vice versa, especially with InstaTwitBook, which I half-heartedly employ in a tepid attempt to reach more people with my songs. The implied tether between social media 'engagement' and actual support was probably cut long ago, when I lined their pockets in promotion of a show to people who were already 'followers,' none of which showed up.

I'm just trying to find somebody who'll listen. And somebody is, somewhere, listening to me, and maybe the more beautiful mystery is to not know them as a metric, not know where they came from, or what they're going home to.

What they're going home to.

I wrote a song about that, with a friend here at the house, after one of his shows. He'd played a small listening room downtown, and just before he came onstage, I watched a woman with large sunglasses pick her way with a cane to a reserved seat in the front. I asked the sound man if he knew her, and he said she came to maybe a show a month, and that she was completely blind.

She sang every word.

I stepped outside after the show and saw her waiting at the corner for the bus, which pulled up a few minutes later. She used her cane to make her way up the stairs and into a seat at the front, under the flickering fluorescent bulbs mounted above the advertisements.

And she was gone.

On the drive home, I told Chuck what I'd seen, and after his post-show whiskey, we wrote a song for her, wondering what her place looked like, and if she had anyone waiting for her at home.

The lyrics weren't only just about might've-been's, though.

I sing the chorus in a low murmur, at first hearing my mom in every word.

What's she going home to
Is it a room full of lonesome
In a house full of pain
With a hole in the roof
That lets in the rain
Are there pictures on the wall
Of what used to be
Does she walk the halls haunted
By a sad memory
Has the name on the mailbox been changed
Is she dreaming alone too
What's she going home to

Is that my mom, or me?

Whatever she was going home to, she'd made considerable effort to come hear my friend's songs, this woman who was more than a metric, but a presence, despite, or perhaps because, she couldn't see social media's screen.

I've thought stepping away from social media, now that the toxicity to curated lifestyle ratio seems to be approaching 1:1. Those in the business of low-hanging artist-marketing fruit keep telling me a social media presence can't hurt, but their reasoning generally comes down to not *why*, but *why not?*

I realized *why not* yesterday, when I checked out a singer-songwriter on social media, saw that he had more posts than followers, and immediately declared his songs less good, his story less deserving of attention.

If he didn't have InstaTwitBook, searches by interested fans would lead somewhere else, probably to his website, where they might buy an album, or see when he's playing in their town, instead of glancing at a less-than-robust social media feed, and moving on.

That's *why not.*

How did this subtle, sometimes imperceptible, always stupid, instant judgement get ingrained into our psyche? Why would we automatically assign artistic worth based on these metrics, as if those profiles parading higher numbers have earned some sort of social proof, when all they've really earned is valuable data for their chosen muse?

But that's what that artist was told to do: mine his social media mountains, which are really mole hills, over and over and over, until he had to don his headlamp and drop down the shaft of InstaTwitBook.

Or bend over.

I wish I could give that singer-songwriter permission to abandon this reluctant, false obligation. I want to allow them to embrace the mystery and dedication of those artists in Laurel Canyon, before social media, when they hustled to offer their developed craft in person, to an actual human being, no matter the cost or sacrifice.

Because to affect deep change in one person is more profound and fulfilling than to be a momentary blur across the screen of many.

Ok, me.

Permission granted.

EMILY

My stomach rumbles again, impatient with these conversations with myself, so I head toward the kitchen, pausing in front of an envelope resting patiently on the bench by the front door. I've passed by this missive postmarked Connecticut for the last few days without stopping, just another dirty sock on the ground, ignored for no reason.

I open up the envelope, and autumn leaves fall from between two pieces of paper, onto the wide-planks of wood at my feet.

A real handwritten letter.

Dear Alex,

Every year around this time, I feel a little nostalgic and sad, because this is the season when I lost someone who meant a great deal to me. You see, I am one of the lucky ones, I have experienced the amazing connection of love with a soul mate. A real kindred spirit. Unfortunately, he passed away a few years ago, but I still consider myself lucky, not only because I have felt true love, but I have lost it as well and that too can be considered a gift; for I now know even more than before just how precious life and love are.

Of course, I am not always able to smile through the day, sometimes I still miss him, painfully so. Like in Autumn, not only the time of year when he was taken from me, but also the time we loved best. So, every year around this time, when the memories fill me, I write him a letter. I thought I'd share it with you, not so you'd write a song for he and I, but because I think your songs are gifts. Pieces of yourself used to help other people with their stories. So, here is a piece of myself. It is all I have to share in return for the wonderful thing you are doing with your music and your talent.

Emily

Well, I have at least one fan. One incredible fan.

Dear Anno,

The leaves have begun to change again. it began a few weeks ago, but with a subtlety I am not sure I can describe. As if Nature was planning a surprise party, for weeks the plans go on behind your back, bit by bit. Then suddenly one morning you walk outside and the brisk autumn air screams "SURPRISE!" You look up and see all the colors, like old friends; orange, umber, yellow, sienna, burgundy, green and brown. The trees are ablaze in a patchwork of fiery brilliance that comforts your very soul.

My favorite coffee shop has pumpkin coffee now. I drink it down in gulps that fill my thoughts with memories of autumns past when we carved funny faces in pumpkins and ate caramels as we walked in the woods looking for pinecones. We were so young then, so happy and free spirited. I still feel that way sometimes. It's like a cosmic gift from the universe. It doesn't happen often, but when it does- Oh, the feeling! Like an orgasm for the soul when you feel alive and free of worry. When doubt and fear are strangers to you and you remember what fun feels like. Do you remember fun? We used to have lots of it this time of year; jumping in leaf piles and laughing, hot apple cider flowing in our veins, the smell of cinnamon and spice in the air.

It lasted only a short time before the season of hot cocoa and snow-flakes would quickly drift in and frost over our little world, but while it lasted, autumn was a happy time. We were young and in love and the world was beautiful.

I still miss you, you know, when the trees are on fire my heart yearns for you. When the night becomes chilled and the hot apple cider is sipped around the bonfires, I still think of you. Sometimes, I swear I can feel your arms wrap around me at night when I stand out in the cold. The cool night wind tickles my neck like the scruff of your unshaved face as we cuddled close to the fire.

I don't know where the soul goes when a person dies, but I hope it is Autumn where you are too and that you think of me sometimes when the leaves blow off the trees and the jack-o-lanterns are smil-ing.

I miss you.

Forever,
Your Em

I touch the brittle leaves and ink-stained paper.

I can't let these words go unanswered.

Another handwritten letter sent to me went unanswered once, the sender telling me that I was the one she wanted to spend her life with, and always had been, but now she was ready, and would move the earth to put us on the same page: couples counseling, whatever it took.

But if she didn't hear back from me, she'd know to move on.

I only found out the letter was even written years later, when *Her* called to let me know she was getting married. I was sort of surprised, and told her that I always thought we'd meet at the same place and time, somewhere down the road, and finally walk together.

She said it was her turn to be surprised, because she'd poured her heart out in that letter to me, written by hand to express deeper ritual and permanence, but she never heard back, and had taken the hint to move on.

What letter? I asked.

And this how the biggest of ships can cross in the night, where the ship is love and the night is an underfunded postal service.

So I'm going to respond to this one.

I want to write more than a few lines in a thank you note, though.

She sees her loss through a lens of love, joy, and gratitude, aware of these gifts, and these are the gifts I want to be aware of too, this is the lens I want to look through, made from the sand of gratitude melted into liquid joy, cooled by love, until the glass gently reflects the past and brilliantly focuses the future.

My wondering gaze trains a searchlight on the end of the first letter.

I thought I'd share it with you, not so you'd write a song for he and I, but because I think your songs are gifts. Pieces of yourself used to help other people with their stories. So, here is a piece of myself.

The answer is there, in what she didn't intend for me to do.

A friend who has sold a gajillion records, and has a Grammy holding court on his toilet tank, lives nearby, and a few minutes later I'm knocking on his door.

I hand him the envelope, and tell him my idea.

My own Laurel Canyon breeze is at my back as I walk home up the driveway, gaze set on the barrel-paver-roof-tile Taj Mahal. I wonder if the mama bird has found the nest since last night, when I last checked on the hidden stash of six squirming chicks.

Their eyes had gained light over the last few weeks, feathers developed from tiny fibrous stubs, and they looked more like birds than babies. But their beaks were still strained upward for food, small pleas breaking the otherworldly quiet that follows the east wind blowing through this little valley.

For every season, turn, turn, turn

Maybe the time for a mother's nurturing has passed.

THIRTEEN

On the way into the house through the garage, I notice a tattered cardboard box tipped against the wall by the water heater, flaps open to expose whatever remember-when's didn't qualify for the chest under the bedroom window. I must've knocked this over with the truck when I came back from Trader Joe's, lost in spiraling thoughts about my old friend with his trash bags in the middle of the street.

A small red sleeve peeks out from the lower corner.

L'il Alex.

I was named after my dad, who wasn't a giant himself, but bigger than me. Seeking a differential when yelling at us, my mom landed on *Little Alex*. This moniker unfortunately had staying power, and some cruel, deservedly unremembered bastard gave me a shirt for Christmas with a bubbled *Lil Alex* ironed-on across my tiny chest, which apparently wouldn't accommodate the word *Little*. The same cruel bastard supplied my dad with a *Big Alex* version, and when we wore them together, we looked like that couple that have the matching *I'm with stupid* pointing-arrow shirts.

My mom suggested I wear that shirt to Disneyland for my late-June birthday, so I'd be easily identifiable when I inevitably turned up on the theme park missing persons report. I was taking my new best friend Doug Wilson, who was also small, and also horrified at the prospect of going to Disneyland with those bubbled iron-on letters anywhere in our orbit.

I mean, we were 13 now.

We'd just finished eighth grade two days before, when David Bartoli handed back my *Mustang Memories* yearbook, his thin lips peeled into a glistening saliva smirk.

He watched expectantly for a knowing nod as I read, but unfortunately, being of innocent mind and undeveloped body, I had no idea what his poorly punctuated run-on sentence meant.

Summers a beaver hunt so go get some.

Beavers occasionally floated through my Ranger Rick nature magazines, gripping unlucky fish between their toothy paws, as they rolled in suspended motion through watery climes. And until this 8th-grade juncture, the word *summer* had meant dreaded day camps, punctuated by Star Wars action-figure battles bloodying the brown shag carpet of my bedroom.

Combining summer and beavers seemed incongruous. And hunting? I'd learned from Ranger Rick that trapping season was in the fall, when the weather cooled.

Doug's older brother had interpreted David Bartoli's message as a missive dedicated to finding hot babes, which seemed like a reasonable next step for two undersized, late-to-the-party almost-pubescent tweens. We determined that hot babes would not be into the *L'il Alex* moniker, unless it was a porn star name I'd had to assume to get work, since I was technically underage, and apparently undersized.

The shirt stayed home, and we roamed Disneyland freer than we'd ever been, with no parents to check in with for eight whole hours.

Hot babes waited in front of us in line for Space Mountain, but they were tall.

Hot babes waited behind us in line for churros, but they were talking to lightly-mustached, hair-parted-in-the-middle guys who probably had pubic hair.

And hot babes sat right next to us, in our row on Small World, but we turned toward each other and Ro-Sham-Boed for who had to talk to them first, until the birds were singing Dixie on the riverboat, and the ride was over.

The beaver hunt ended with Doug falling asleep in the backseat of my mom's car, and me staring out the window, wondering where we could possibly learn how to trap properly.

Doug's older brother agreed to hold a tutorial the next afternoon in their garage, while he was lifting weights and smoking a sad-looking cigarette twisted at the ends. But I wasn't there to analyze his confusing-smelling tobacco choice.

I was there for a hunting answer, which really boiled down to a question.

What's your number?

This, according to Doug's older brother, who seemed a lot like an older David Bartoli, was the genesis of all beaver hunts, the bait that set the trap.

I had to get a phone number, any phone number.

So, imagine my horrified delight, when I realized I already had the most beautiful girl in the world's phone number.

Jenny Cooper.

She would appear at monumental junctures in my younger life, in a story told before, from my first date to my first dance to my first time, my first *I Love You* to my first heartbreak, my first window into the ravages of crystal meth.

And my first, and only deep connection, until *Her.*

I'd sat next to Jenny Cooper during eighth grade World Geography class. She had worn a real bra, lip gloss, and her hair was gelled back like Molly Ringwald. She winked and smiled at me on the first day of school, inspiring the intentional accident of running into her by the lockers at precise intervals throughout the year. We'd talk about her weekend plans and my lack thereof, and in the spaces between breaths, I'd mine the unforgiving hard clay of my experience, gleaned mostly from *An Officer and a Gentleman*, searching for veins of love gold to offer. I'd walk away from those locker conversations comforting myself that I was probably still going around with Jennifer Nystrom, anyway, and didn't want to start a tendency toward infidelity this early.

After Jenny, David Bartoli, Doug, and a handful of disinterested comrades signed my yearbook on the last day of school, I discovered that she'd slipped her phone number on a torn piece of Pee-Che folder into the pages, with a note about getting lunch the next Saturday.

So, I had a phone number.

And a reason to call.

All I needed was to unlock some semblance of courage, and the Audi Fox musical revelation the previous summer held the key. Early that July Saturday morning, I took my position next to our Realistic 91 Clarinette AM/FM turntable and cassette deck combo, with my sister's vinyl copy of Journey's *Escape* already locked and loaded, auditory bullets ready to fire. Arming myself with the Koss Pro 4AA wrap-around headphones, I cranked the volume, lifted the needle...

And pulled the trigger.

I fought strong and deep in the first two tracks of Side A, where I was just a city boy born and raised in south Detroit, where burning love came once in a lifetime, over and over and over, until there was no way I'd stop believing, because I was stone in love.

Battle-weary yet sufficiently victorious, I hit Stop on the Realistic, took off the headphones, and exploded into the kitchen, where our rotary telephone waited on top of the directory perched in the dinette nook.

I frantically dialed *424-2054*, but hung up as soon as the last 4 spun around.

All hundred pounds of my sister were thumping the floor above me to a song cranked on her Radio Shack hifi. Some guy was telling a girl named Jenny that he got her number and needed to make her his, that he tried to call her before but he lost his nerve.

I hadn't yet learned that *serendipity* was a hippie way of saying *coincidence*, but as *867-5309* serendipitously thundered through the house, the singer started sounding more like me. His *867-5309* was my *424-2054*. His lost nerve was mine. His Jenny was, too.

The repeating coda faded into radio static, as the DJ's tenor circled above a majestic piano chord and note interplay. This masterpiece had just guided me on the battlefield moments ago, but instead of one of the greatest rock voices of all time suggesting that I don't stop believin', Steve Perry whispered from my right shoulder.

Dude, she wants to talk to you. She gave you her number. DUDE.

Thirty minutes later, Jenny and I met at a burger place within walking distance of our houses, where I ordered food for the first time without an adult around. We waited for our number to be called, picked up the styrofoam cups and mesh plastic baskets lined with wax paper, and sat down across from each other in the cockpit of an X-Wing fighter.

When our greasy fingers touched in a mutual reach for fries, the spaceship dove in a thrilling, breathless drop, until Jenny moved her foot under the table to rest against my shin and the rocket ship banked right, until she reached across the table with a napkin to wipe stray mustard from my cheek and the X-wing accelerated up into the heavens, on a mission to destroy the Death Star of pubescent hell.

And I lived inside every single sweaty special awkward moment, as if that beautiful scene in space and time might never come again.

This was no beaver hunt.

This was a spiritual rocket-ship, fueled by poetic propulsion... lyric and verse, steeped in meaning and devoid of casual emptiness, which I thought about the rest of July and all of August, hoping Jenny might call, because I wasn't sure if I was supposed to call her, until she went to a different high school and left me to search for the same song, for most of the rest of my life, at least until I met *Her* and started the whole dance all over again.

Summer would never be a beaver hunt to me.

Not like David Bartoli meant, anyway.

August ended on a dripping hot Friday, and my friend and I decided going surfing would be the best summer sayonara. I did, unexpectedly, have another friend, besides Doug Wilson.

Throughout my shy life, I'd been told that I needed to make friends, but I'd found the fabrication of friends yielded fleeting surface relationships that could disappear on a peer-influenced whim. Over the past seven summers, though, the slightly older kid down the alley and I played handball against the neighbor's wall, and basketball with the bachelor across the street, and jumped our skateboards over cracks in the asphalt.

We just did fun stuff together.

Which made us friends.

He was sixteen and drove a massive 1969 Plymouth Fury III, with a trunk big enough to fit surfboards. We mourned the last true day of summer on the ride to our local break, where we found a parking place big enough to accommodate a small boat and carried our boards down to The River.

Not Springsteen's *River*... the San Gabriel river mouth, teeming with stingrays and inexplicably warmer than anyplace else. We willingly took the risk of having to pee on ourselves if we got stung, in exchange for being able to wear trunks like we were in Hawaii.

I was getting better at standing up, but the process still took too long. By the time I'd finally climb to my feet, back knee then front knee, back foot then front foot, the wave had always already broken, so I'd be resigned to riding the whitewater.

And this was not really surfing. Surfing was gliding along the actual wave, the curl of broken whitewater behind, open face in front, gloriously moving forward in two directions, toward the beach and across the water.

I'd never had that feeling.

We made our way around the jetty and out to the river mouth, where I paddled for a waist-high offering and started to laboriously push to my feet. My first attempt was always more of a struggle, and by the time I finally rose to my feet in frustrated anticipation, I knew the wave would die out within a few seconds.

Except the wave didn't die out.

Because my takeoff had taken forever, I was farther inside the river mouth than I'd been before. I didn't know that the whitewater here often faded into another steepening swell, the same energy becoming a brand-new breaking wave.

Sometimes, waves reform.

And now I was riding the open face, for the first time, my mouth agape in joy and astonishment. In a sudden ill-advised rush of confidence, I turned the blue G&S thruster toward the lip, like I'd seen in surf videos, and immediately fell.

Didn't matter.

I was surfing.

summers a Beaver
hunt so go get
some

FOR THE SENDER

I set the box upright, tucking the red sleeve under the folded flaps, along with a different day's story of remember-when's. As I open the door into the house, I instinctively step over the bare spot where the big brown dog used to leave her slobbered tennis ball, empty space that will soon be filled with tiny chew toys, and probably a puddle or two.

I told Claire I'd pick the little yellow puppy on my way home from the airport in a couple of days, so I start puppy-proofing obvious issues while letting others slide, because some things are going to get wrecked no matter what. I leave the remote controls within reach on the couch, but unplug an abandoned Christmas light extension cord, which I'm wrapping into a warped ring when an email dings from my phone.

I hang the extension cord in the garage and head to the living room couch, where I reply with a cautiously excited, anticipatory smile and two exchanges later, we have it, including a rough demo recorded on a phone.

hello my friend
it's me again
writing words i can not send you

autumn's cold
the leaves are old
and letting go but not me

cause it's when we met
and its when you left
and its when our love was the best
so every year
i write you this letter
like a prayer
its more for the sender

sometimes i swear
you're in the air
am i just a great
pretender

am i alone
i want to know
do you like to remember

cause it's when we met
and its when you left
and its when our love was the best
so every year
i write you this letter
like a prayer
its more for the sender

do you remember

A song.

For the sender.

TREADING WATER

My 1969 Gibson B25 leaning against the couch cushions creaks in mild protest as I grab the headstock and lay her in my lap. I listen to the phone recording, trying to learn the chords and sing the melody, which seems to only corrupt the purity and rawness of my friend's version.

Sounds ok to me.

Mom?

Hi honey.

What are you doing here?

You know I'm always around. I might not talk like I used to, but I haven't really gone anywhere.

I just…

Shhhh. It's ok. Look, I brought you another photograph from that chest, to make you laugh… this one, when you fell up the stairs.

Up, not down?

Well, you were always falling when you were small. Down the stairs, too, but this one is pretty great.

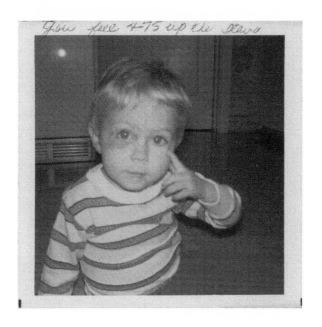

I'm pointing to the wrong eye.

Must not have hurt that bad. That's what I thought when you crashed into the neighbor's wall on your bike with training wheels, too.

With my eyes closed.

Right, with your eyes closed, day before Easter. Your friend from down the alley had to run into the house three times before I finally came out and saw your forearm bone sticking out of your skin. I usually assumed crying was just complaining.

Yeah, I learned to not do much of either of those.

I know, I'm sorry. You got that from me... I had to be the strong, stoic one, especially for my little sister, in foster care and in the Masonic home. You have to do what you have to do to survive when things get dark.

And they never did for me, not really, because of you and dad. I had such a different childhood. I was thinking about that today, looking at some of those photographs. How lucky I was.

We weren't going to let history repeat.

You could have easily made things as hard for me as they were for you.

And what would that have done? Somehow legitimized what I went through? I might not have always wanted kids, but I wasn't going to be that person.

I do remember you telling me that if you had to do it over again, you probably wouldn't have had kids. I wasn't sure how to take that.

Well, you know I love you, very deeply.

I know.

But as far back as I can remember, I never really got to do what I wanted to do. I didn't have much of a childhood since I was taking care of my sister, living under those harsh institutional rules until high school, when I met your dad and had you and your sister. He wanted kids so bad, and I wanted to give that to him. And then I went to work the rest of my life for my mom, who'd given me up, and she was still just so angry and mean. I cried on the drive home from the office most nights.

You hid all of that.

I had to keep our little world turning. And that's really all I meant by not having kids again. I just didn't think I deserved time for myself, at all, ever, to figure out what I wanted to do. Never felt like I had a choice, I guess, especially after you and your sister were born.

DANCE

You did so many little beautiful, thoughtful things, though.

I wasn't going to not be your mom! You need to remember those good times for me, when I can't. That's why I brought this out-of-focus photograph of when I played Alice in your elementary school Alice in Wonderland play. I think I made the costume. I also think they only asked me because I had the right hair for the part.

Yeah, but I'm talking about the even smaller things, like making my lunch every morning before you went to work, wrapping the carrots and celery and Skippy peanut butter sandwich in Saran Wrap, arranging everything in my Grizzly Adams lunch box. Even with a napkin. Maybe a brownie. And sometimes a note, or one of those *Love Is* comics cut out of the newspaper. That reminds me. I have a confession.

About what?

About lunch.

Ok.

Before we were allowed to play at lunchtime in elementary school, we had to show that we'd finished our lunch.

And?

Sometimes I'd throw away part of my lunch, because I was so excited to run around. Not the whole thing. But still.

And now you're feeling guilty, decades later?

Well, yeah. I mean, you put your heart into making those lunches. And I just threw them away.

And you found out how that felt later on, didn't you? Putting your heart into something, only to have it thrown away.

How did you know?

I listened to your songs. You might not have thought I did. But I did.

Kind of silly, but I still feel a little stab in my stomach, when that image floats through my memory of hiding half of a peanut butter sandwich in my hand on the way to the trash can. I guess I'm sorry for that, even now. Especially now, that, you know…

What? Now that I can't make lunches anymore?

Yeah.

You know, what's happening to me isn't all bad.

Yes, it is.

No, it's not. If I get mad at your father, it's never for long, because I forget the reason why so quickly. I used to hold grudges over his head like an anvil, but now the anger dissipates almost immediately. And in its place rises some sort of peace I never had before.

Because I'm finally kind of doing what I want to do. I always wanted to take the world off my shoulders, to go on a walk with your dad and then sit in a chair and watch the trees dancing in the wind. I can do that now.

And speaking of dancing, when Waylon Jennings or Willie Nelson comes on the radio, I just dance, wherever I am, twirling around, hands on my hips, or up in the air. I never danced in the first 70 years of my life. I didn't feel like I was allowed to let go like that. Moving my body, expressing whatever's in here, however it looks, without judging myself? No way.

Never did I dance.

But I do now.

LOVE IS

There's just so much that's so hard. For me, for you, for dad.

I know. I just wanted to tell you there are a few silver linings. And do you really want to spend whatever time we have left being sad about what you can't change? This isn't some burden you can unload. It's just part of the deal. Part of living. Part of you.

So basically, you're telling me to let go of throwing away my lunch when I was in elementary school.

Listen. When I was at the Masonic home, they had a strict rule that we had to eat everything on our plate, and if we didn't, we'd be sent to sit in the broom closet during playtime.

I remember your broom closet stories.

Right. Well, I hated chicken, because one of my chores in foster care had been collecting eggs and picking up after the family's chickens, which pecked my hands raw. Also, I saw that the eggs came out of the same place as the poop, which made me hate eggs, too.

And I'm guessing the Masonic home served a lot of chicken and eggs?

All the time. So when no one was looking, I'd hide the nastiness in my lap. By the time the meal was over, I'd have a clean plate. And a bulging napkin to hide on my way out of the dining hall.

Kind of like half of a peanut butter sandwich in Saran Wrap.

Exactly like that.

I always kept the *Love Is* comic though.

That was my way of saying I love you.

So is bringing you this last photograph.

This is how I remember you.

I still do, you know.

I love you too, Mom.

IT

I know where I am, but not how I got here, only who I walked with.

She brings me photographs. Of younger times, before I grew older, but I may be growing younger again, photographs for the ancient family slide projector that would be set up in the living room on homemade hot fudge sundae picture nights, now whirring and clicking, as images fill the battered silver screen of my memory.

I ask her questions, but she answers in my voice.

And so, she doesn't bring me photographs the way a mother brings a wet washcloth to a sick child.

Sometimes I wish she could.

The photograph floats to the side of the chest, where a tattered square bar-paper-napkin note is wedged in the corner, crowning a pile of printouts and envelopes.

You were great, have one on me.

When I was getting started in dive-bars and taverns back in Seattle, I rarely let the clear water of this kind of acknowledgement sink in deep enough to satisfy my thirst for 'making it.' I thought a platinum-selling album and sold-out tour were the best way to show my parents, and myself, that I had made the right decision in quitting my job to pursue a career in music.

And so these letters, written to my downtown Seattle post office box, and emails sent through my late-90s rudimentary single-page website, landed here, in a haphazard stack, now barely held together by a played-out length of elastic.

Some part of me had enough sense to keep these kind words written by strangers. The rest of me, which considered myself a minor failure for not getting that platinum-selling album and sold-out tour, took awhile to catch up to what really matters.

This long, until right now, standing in front of this open chest, holding this bar napkin and finally allowing myself to absorb these gifts, these flowers grown from the seeds of true fans, who might've driven across the state to see me play, or bought whatever five-song EP I'd put together, had I played to them, rather than to the stars.

Like this guy, Tuffer, twenty-four years ago.

I caught your show a couple months back at the Showbox and loved it. Since then, though, I kept looking for your shows but can't find them in the various club listings. Luckily I just found your website and concert dates so I'm excited about being able to catch more shows. Props go to you for having the smarts to put your info out there on the web.

I'd also love any info on shows, CDs, etc you have available. I did pick up your EP at the Showbox show, though I only had a couple of dollars in my wallet so that's all I put down for it (you were encouraging people just to take them anyways). But I would like to send the full price for it, if that's possible. I'm sure it takes money to make it big and that would suck if you can't finance that cuz punks like me only plunk down $2 for a CD you paid to make yourself.

Good luck and I look forward to hearing more of the band.

All I really needed were a few more Tuffers.

That's all I need now.

I have to be at the airport in a few hours, so I take a quick shower and start packing for the trip, which amounts to a gig bag with some clothes wedged on either side of my guitar, and a backpack for my computer and whatever CDs I won't sell. People don't really buy CDs anymore, at least not mine.

Hard to sell what I give away.

But I still have it in me, you know? To deliver a message across a vast expanse, to carry a theater or a stadium there with me, reveling and celebrating and mourning and honoring all that is life in a mess of guitars and drums.

I didn't put it there, though.

See that padded envelope, next to the pajamas?

I'd moved to Boston right out of college, because the city felt historic and different, and also because the dream university that had rejected me was in the area. I wanted to prove to myself that I belonged there, I guess, and would sometimes walk the campus pretending I'd been accepted.

I found a soul-sucking entry-level position in the financial district, where I commuted every morning on the T with a throng of workers who looked just as unhappy as me.

I thought that's what I was supposed to do.

I went home for Christmas break, and one morning after surfing, sunk myself into my cousin's couch in his rented beach house. I'd found a cheap nylon-strung guitar in the corner, and was banging out the three chords I knew the best to words I'd written in my loft apartment in Boston, about a homeless guy I'd seen on the subway.

A friend of my cousin's emerged from the hallway and asked me when my next show was.

Show?

Yeah, where are you playing?

I've never played a show.

What?

I don't even know how to book a show, let alone play one.

Are you kidding?

No.

What do you do for a living?

I work in an office. Well, more in a cubicle.

You should be doing what you're doing here on the couch.

I don't know…

You're brilliant. Has anyone told you that?

No. I mean, I don't really let anyone hear me.

You should.

She visited me in Boston that January, I visited her in Oregon that March, and over every phone call in between, in all these letters, she shined a light on my artist's path, telling me that I could play arenas someday, if I'd open up to the idea, kept writing and practicing, and *for F's sake, play a show.*

Early that April, I woke up to a Bruce Springsteen song called

113

"Trapped" on my alarm clock radio, which was my final push out of the concrete walls of the city. Two weeks later I was driving across the country to live with her on the Columbia River Gorge.

I pulled up to her house, windows darkened.

Maybe she's in bed, I thought.

I knocked on the door.

No answer.

She knew I was coming.

Why wasn't she here?

Even the door was locked.

I let myself in through the bedroom window, and brought in the black Labrador puppy I'd picked up along the way in Utah.

The next morning, the clerk at the local grocery store, who'd asked if I was new to town and where I was staying, told me she'd gone to Mexico on a photo shoot. He thought she'd mentioned something about a boat before she left, so who knew when she'd be back.

That black Lab puppy and I lived at her house for almost two months, before cell phones, waiting for her to come home.

Late one mid-June night, headlights blasted the driveway and swooped across the bedroom wall, but I thought I was dreaming, and quickly fell back asleep. When I woke up at dawn, she was passed out on the couch, snoring softly.

She'd fallen in sudden love with the boat captain, and had spent the last month and a half cruising through the crystalline waters of paradise.

Three hours later, I'd packed up my puppy and my life, and headed north to Seattle, where another cousin had another couch waiting for me.

I took what she'd given me up I-5, too.

And I had it in me back when the dream seemed within reach, that summer when the neighborhood gathered in my living room, because the video for my song might go to #1 on CMT's countdown, which happened, then again, and again. I had it in me back when I opened a letter from SXSW, then the holy grail of festivals, inviting me to perform as a featured artist, back when the 1000 person room fell silent as I whispered a chorus, back when I had them in my hand, back when they had me in their heart.

Tomorrow night I'll be at the same venue in Austin, only this time in the lounge, off the main stage, where I'll be setting up in the corner and playing for whoever's sitting at the pub tables, because one night this town lifted me higher toward my dream, and maybe the undercurrent will rise again.

Sometimes, waves reform.

Not always.

Because I'm still riding the same crumbled, weakening whitewater, the dying energy not of a dream, but a way of doing things, when maybe I just need to step off the board, paddle back out, and catch another wave.

And then I find small reminders of why I'm still riding, hesitant to pull out of this wave, like this email I got before I started packing:

Alex,

Recall that day in Hermosa. You. Guitar. And a wordsmith pounding out brilliance about a homeless man looking for love in a subway.

And then it was gone. The subway song.

Grateful for you and your passion to follow your heart.

Few choose.

That alone is inspiring.

Xo

E.

I had it in me then, and I have it in me now.

She put it there.

HOPE

I reach for the latch to close the lid, but now that I've opened up my chest to show a glimpse of what made me, of what I hold close, I suppose I could let what's inside breathe newer air for awhile.

I handwrite the "For The Sender" lyrics on a sheet of printer paper and search for an envelope to send to Emily, which I find in a box of office supplies my parents gave me when they moved north to the mountains. I copy her return address onto the envelope, drop the lyrics inside, and tuck the letter under the tiny loop of leather in my backpack. I'll send the letter from the terminal, and will want the collar when I pick up the little yellow puppy after this trip.

I throw my gig bag and backpack in the back seat, and climb into my truck to head to the airport. A hawk drops in front of my hood as I pull down the driveway, clutching a tiny bird culled from, hopefully, one of the eucalyptus trees bordering the house.

I put the transmission into reverse and back up until I'm even with the makeshift shelter, jump out of the driver's seat, and duck the fence to check on the baby birds. My pocket vibrates a stride later, and while I stall in front of the nest, afraid I'll see one less chick, I check the text.

My eyes drop immediately to the farewell signature.

Da mu(b) er lernen von den Dingen,
anfangen wieder wie ein Kind
weil sie, die Gott am Herzen hingen,
nicht von ihm fortgegangen sind.

Eins mu(b) wieder konnen: fallen,
geduldig in der Schwere ruhn,
der sich verma(b), den Vogeln allen
im Fliegen es zuvorzutun . . .

My last message to you.

Goodbye.

Your friend,
Rilke

I text back a question mark and wait a few breaths.

Nothing.

I tentatively peek into the small alcove to confirm my worst-case-scenario fear, and a sudden ruffling startles me backward into the same surprised reaction that made me drop the little egg, as can other eruptions of new life, disruptions in too-comfortable norms, shifting focus from sleepwalking into the present.

Here, where these six small pieces of hope have finished their incubation, because they fly out of the shelter one at a time, dropping every so slightly inches from my chest, before lifting and disappearing into the late afternoon sky.

RILKE

I still have a couple of hours before my flight, so I sit on the stairs spilling from the house to the yard, interpreting the choppy translation results into the notebook I took from the truck still idling in the driveway.

My heart is thumping against my skin, harder and harder with each line, because now I know who's been trying to reach me.

The poet tucked away in my chest.

Rainer Marie Rilke, straddling the 19th century and countries and lovers, unknown in his present but revered in his past, who in that book, *Letters to a Young Poet,* wrote, *If you will stay close to nature, to its simplicity, to the small things hardly noticeable, those things can unexpectedly become great and immeasurable.*

An eerie prescience accompanies almost every phrase now and I sheepishly look around, as if he could be following me, because how else would he know about the birds, how would he know about my heaviness, the weight of slow loss I long to lighten.

We have to learn like children
Who never left God's heart
The smallest thing fallen
Is where we too must start
Heaviness is true and just
And where our freedom lies
As a bird must fall and trust
His weight before he flies

Maybe he's right.

Maybe I don't need to lighten the weight of slow loss.

Because maybe the heaviness isn't a burden, only proof I'm alive, already strong enough to stand up and carry this weight to the peak of the next glorious mountain crag, from which I will fall.

And let my better angel fly.

Down the freeway, where I'm trying to remember why I'm leaving.

I know I'm supposed to get on a plane, to play songs in another town for people that may not show up, because they have jobs, or kids, or fights, or long-running happy hours, or shows to watch on Netflix.

Which I understand.

They aren't as deeply tethered to my songs, as I was to songs by artists I couldn't even name at the time. Like Tom Petty's "Even the Losers," that can awaken an eleven-year-old to the idea that music can actually carry a message. Or The Cult's "She Sells Sanctuary," that lift a far-from-pubescent tween into rarefied air, where he might write a song of his own. Or even Tommy Tutone's "867-5309," affirming that a rock singer's anxious story of numbers written on a wall can be a barely-teenager's awkward pursuit, too.

And of course, Journey's "Don't Stop Believin," that can inspire a thirteen-year-old to stand up... but even I knew who that band was back then.

I take the airport off-ramp on autopilot, this mecca of leaving ingrained in my GPS DNA from years of leaving. Touring is part of the expected process of writing, recording, and playing songs, to a modest level of success, the way bathwater is barely warm enough to stay in, but not hot enough to actually enjoy. These trips have become suitcases on the airport baggage claim carousel, all different but the same, carelessly arranged and spaced one after the other, and mostly spent wondering if I've lost what are supposed to be the best years of my life canvasing the country, asking people to like me.

Which is another way to say *performing.*

And that's not what I wanted this to be about, back when I started, when I played "Revolve" in that cramped Seattle living room for *Her.* I wanted to tether my heart to someone else's, not shoot in the dark at a million people on the opposite shore, hoping a few take a bullet.

Maybe my own purer beginning has devolved into just another

before, as I've towed the line of expectation, doing what everyone else was doing, wanting what everyone else wanted, because that's what comes next, that's what progress looks like, that's what success looks like, until I became no different than the impostors with their heroin and blow who invaded Laurel Canyon and turned a beautiful beginning into a wistfully mourned *before*.

Emily, though.

"For The Sender."

A song just for her, a tether to her heart. Like "Revolve," for *Her*.

But this is also a letting go, because the song is her story, not mine, which has freed me from being locked in a cage of my own introspective construction.

"For The Sender" could be another beginning.

I crawl through traffic entering the airport, now about a car-length away from an older man on the curb holding a *Homeless and Hungry Vet, Anything Helps* sign. The truck in front of me doesn't move to make up the few inches of available space, and my breath quickens, my forehead collapses in confused frustration, and my chin drops to my chest, as the muscles in my forearm tense and quiver, tense and quiver, and I don't know what's happening, but there are two of me in here, because this is his breath quickening, his forehead collapsing, his chin dropping to his chest, the muscles in his forearm tensing and quivering, tensing and quivering, until my body releases into his and he is waving me ahead.

I pull around and check the rear-view mirror, just as the driver reaches over through the passenger window and gives the *Anything Helps* guy a grease-stained brown paper bag.

That looks like the guy in the gray t-shirt.

I don't know, maybe not.

He seemed angry before, not really the giving type.

Unless that's not really him.

RED LIGHT

I finally get to the signal by the terminal just as the light turns red. I watch travelers drift in front of my truck's hood, trudging to their rental cars or own cars or other people's cars, their heads at right angles to their bodies, staring down at their phones. They're programmed, just like me, living within the four walls of their hand-held device, one side built with well-designed dopamine bricks, the other with sturdy confirmation bias, one side with rigid comparative happiness, the other false narratives.

A mid-life-ish man walks behind the rest, carrying a surfboard bag over his shoulder, a perfect mirror of myself in this same crosswalk after I'd planned a trip for my family to Hawaii at Christmas. I'd hoped the island would be familiar to my mom, to the more ancient her, the her when she was a working mother to my sister and me, a tireless wife to our dad, and that place was an escape, a reward, a small breath of softer air.

Maybe she'd remember.

My parents flew from their mountain town, so I traveled separately. I sat in tarmac meditation before the plane took off, my silent mantra fixated on thoughts rotating around whether this trip was actually a good idea.

A small voice interrupted the noise.

Do you believe in Santa Claus?

I looked from the tray table to the little girl in a puffy pink jacket sitting next to me. She'd been in my seat when I boarded the plane, and I'd told her as much, so she'd fumbled with her seatbelt and slid over to the aisle.

I'd forgotten how much I loved the window seat when I was a kid, so I asked her if she wanted to switch and she said, *Yes please and thank you* and that her parents were sitting together somewhere else, but she was a big girl now, and could sit by herself.

She scooted back over, and I settled into the aisle seat. She unwrapped a beat-up Hershey's chocolate bar she'd just pulled from her coat pocket, broke off half, and held it out to me.

Do you want to share?

She introduced me to her stuffed animal, and we spent the first half of the flight playing Rock Paper Scissors and talking about the important things.

She asked me if I was married and then why I wasn't. She guessed my age and I guessed hers. I showed her a picture of my big brown dog and she asked me if I was sure my dog wasn't really a camel.

She inquired if I believed in Santa, and told me she'd asked him for three things: to be good, to be able to study hard, and to be with her mama forever.

My breath caught in my throat at the last request, because I was watching my own mama disappear, and there was nothing Santa could do.

The little girl knew she was getting something else from Santa, too, since she had peeked in a bag her mama had brought home last week, and did I think Santa knew she peeked?

She asked me what the tallest mountain in the world is, and I told her most people would say Mt. Everest, although the tallest mountain from the bottom of the ocean was Mauna Kea, which was on the island we were flying to.

Do you think God sits on top of it and watches over me and everyone?

I sat there for a second, wondering if God was watching over my mom, as I looked at this little girl whose heart shined, so full of curiosity and promise and gratitude and sharing and love, all these things I'd thought I'd lost, that were being given back to me by this better angel sitting in seat 17A.

Yes, I think He probably does.

She read the rest of the way, until the plane touched down and rolled to a stop. When the seat belt sign dinged off, she crawled over me into the aisle, and as she started to walk away, she turned back to say that it was nice talking to me, and she hoped I'd have a Merry Christmas.

And then she was gone.

Do I believe in Santa Claus?

If he can look like a little girl in a puffy pink jacket, then yeah.

I guess I do.

I met my parents at the hotel. A few decades had passed since we'd been on that island as a family, so we arranged to surprise my parents with my sister's arrival. She showed up later that afternoon, while my mom and dad were sitting on their lanai, watching the ocean. My dad fought back tears, and the incredulous look on my mom's face told me that she thought maybe she was seeing things, if another part of her mind was leaving her.

And a few minutes later she said something that will stay with me forever, and maybe that's what the little girl in the puffy pink jacket meant, even thought it turned out not to be true.

I forget things. But I won't forget this.

Even though I'd brought a few boards with me, I surfed only once that trip. My window of opportunity opened when the ocean was choppy and ugly, with lightning and rain making things even nastier. I paddled out anyway, because surfing had become my escape valve, my healing return to where I came from, ever since my dad watched me finally stand up on that old G&S thruster.

And I was sleeping on the pull-out couch in the same room as my parents, so I needed a reset.

A whale rose and fell in front of me in the not-so-distance as I made my way through the reef, a fluke emerging on the tail end of a barnacled back's ridge radius. I felt a few tugs beneath me, but my hands touched only water as I paddled, so I guessed my fins were bumping into seaweed.

The waves weren't huge, probably head-high, but Hawaiian ocean power is a lot stronger than California's. I took off on my first wave and the board slid out from under me, prompting a fall and solid pounding.

I told myself that I wasn't used to the board.

I'd figure it out.

But I couldn't stand up. I was back to my 11-year-old self, barely able to push to my knees on the board, wave after wave. Paddling was harder, too. I'd get stuck inside after a beating and power my way through, duck-diving under churning whitewater, only to get dragged farther back.

The last wave I took off on was bigger. Steep, and farther to the left, closer to the reef. The board slid out again and I got crushed, barely missing the exposed coral and taking on a lot of water, enough for a slight panic to rise in my throat.

While I was under, a thick, quiet peace came over me. The ocean was already churning and confused by the storm, but the beneath was still. I floated in suspension, hesitant to return up there, where I'd be tossed around like a small boat in a tempest.

Like I'm tossed around on the surface of things, of loss, of getting older, of digital noise over which I have little influence, fed to me on a device I no longer use as a tool, but as a pacifier.

It's there, if I want to go back.

The stillness.

The beneath.

But what about oxygen?

I shot to the surface for a breath, as another whale rose and fell in the not-so-distance. I managed to get away from the shallower section of reef, and was so tired by then that I rode the next wave on my belly to the beach, frustrated, exhausted, defeated, and lucky to not have gotten hurt.

Just like that day at Huntington Beach when I was eleven.

Except my dad wasn't there to tell me that I didn't stand up.

I carried my board back to the rental car, so mentally and physically drained that I didn't even notice the problem, until I loaded it into the back seat. I'd ripped out the board's fins, probably on that paddle through the reef, and for all intents and purposes was trying to ride a piece of plywood out there. Fins exist solely to give the surfboard stability, grounding in ungrounding territory.

Next time I find myself falling over and over again, I'm going to make sure my fins are there.

Later that afternoon we stopped by the store, and my mom helped a random person in the parking lot with the grocery bags in her cart. My sister and I looked at each other with raised eyebrow, because my mom would never have done that in her past life.

But over the next several days, my mom yelled at my dad's driving, like she always did. She looked disapprovingly at the not-quite-dressed women eating at the table next to us, like she always did. She put her lipstick on before going anywhere, like she always did.

She did a lot of things with just the four us, like she always did.

Which is why, on the way back to the mainland, in the hours before I trudged through this same crosswalk with a similar surfboard bag, a single tear dropped from my cheek to the open tray table.

We only have so much time.

The light turns green, and the truck that had waved me ahead races past on my right, banking into the short-term parking lot, which is also an expensive long-term solution for travelers late for their flight.

And where I'd be pulling in right now, if I'd not just decided at the red light that I'm not going to travel these rutted tracks, worn deep by mindless machinations, because maybe I shouldn't be staying in a mid-tier hotel tonight after stumbling through an uninspired set of songs that used to matter to me, that should still matter at me. Maybe I shouldn't be staring at myself in the hotel bathroom mirror, my eyes more tired, my face more lined, under the harsh fluorescent glare, before retreating to the bed so many others have laid on, scrolling through my phone for reassurance I'm alive.

Because this is sleepwalking, this is peeing on the polyester pantsuits in my parents' dirty clothes hamper.

I will stand up, for what could be in these precious moments I still have, not what may be someday, and take that little yellow puppy home, where she'll cry for her mother tonight, as I have for mine, where I'll comfort her, as she'll comfort me.

And come morning, we'll be lost in the joy of new life, running through our own Laurel Canyon beginning, where baby birds were nurtured by their mother until they, too, were ready to fly.

THE SPACE BETWEEN

The one-way airport road leads left into a graduated U-turn, around taxi stands, long-term parking, and rental car and ride-sharing kiosks. I roll to a stop at a signal hanging above the same continued crosswalk, now empty, and leave a message for the club, saying I can't make the show. They didn't even sell tickets in advance, so I'm confident they'll find someone else to set up in the corner and play for the cover charge.

I'm searching for the hotel's number when the light changes, so I throw the phone on the passenger seat and consider what not cancelling the room or the flight might look like. Empty bed and airplane seat, an intentionally vacant space left at the Thanksgiving table, because somebody isn't coming back, and I'm not coming back either, not like that.

Sometimes, waves reform.

I call Claire from the stacked-up metered freeway on-ramp and ask if there's any way to get the little yellow puppy this afternoon, and she says sure, she has to run an errand down south anyway.

She meets me in the parking lot of a feed store, a rustic barn reminder of when this millionaire's-row coast was home to horses and poinsettia farms.

Claire gently lifts a tiny ball of fur from the front seat, kisses her on the forehead, and says *Have a wonderful life, small one.*

I hold the little yellow puppy at eye level, and for a string of eternity inside a single moment, I am lost in the pure, unblemished and unconditional love radiating from her seal eyes. The kind of love the movies, country songs, and fairy tales say you're supposed to have with another person, in some beautiful ever after. I don't know, maybe some people are supposed to love a dog, or a river, or a horse, or a bird, or a mountain like that.

Like this.

Maybe I am.

I hold her against my heart, like I did the photo of my mom earlier, but this isn't about rehashing the past, this is about recycling the best parts of the past: the joy, love, and gratitude, into now, and tomorrow, and the day after that, the same energy rising into a new wave.

She falls asleep immediately in my arms, so I say goodbye to Claire, slink into the front seat, and lay the puppy on my lap.

Last summer, sitting around the teak table on my parents' patio, my dad asked me if I'd ever heard the song "Desperado." I said yes, I'd covered the song many times and sung those very words.

Desperado why don't you come to your senses
You been out riding fences for so long now

He said that song reminded him of me. And that it was time to come down from my fences, open the gate, and marry the girl I'd been dating for five years, because she was nice and pretty and good to my mom.

Yesterday, before she left with her trailer, she told me what she's known all along: that our lives aren't parallel, only straight lines angled just opposite enough to widen the space between them into infinity.

I pull away from the feed store and drive nowhere in particular, with a little yellow puppy asleep in the space between the steering wheel and my stomach, which has no chance of widening at all.

BORN TO RUN

We don't get very far on the road to nowhere, as her light snore immediately turns to a faint whimper turns to a have-to-pee whine. I pull into a wide-open swath of wild green bordering the feed store lot, likely a close cousin to the wetlands by my house, and carry the little yellow puppy to the grass.

I gently set her down and let her go, confident I can catch her if she tests her freedom. She looks up at me with those big seal eyes and squats, then hops over between my feet and lays down, like she did in front of the stove in Claire's kitchen.

You're a special one, aren't you?

I pick her up, hold her against my heart, and walk back to the truck, struck by how the lens can change in the course of a few hours… should-do to could-do by abandoning a soulless gig, solitude to companionship with this dog, lethargy to inspiration with Emily.

Beginnings.

What if I wrote another song about her letter? What if I got more letters, and wrote more songs? What if I asked my musician friends to help me? What if I could create some sort of project that honors people's stories by writing songs about them?

What if.

Those two words are where everything begins.

Almost forgot.

The letter with the song for Emily is in my backpack.

I carry the little yellow puppy back to the truck, leave her on the passenger seat, and copy Emily's return address onto the envelope. I saw a mailbox in front of the feed store a minute ago… I'll just cut across to the parking lot.

I guess I could see if she'll follow me.

I set her back on the grass, turn around to face her, and take a couple of steps backward.

Backward, but forward.

She willingly stumbles over her paws toward me, all the way to the mailbox, where I push the letter through the slot before squatting down eye-level with the little yellow puppy.

Where to now?

No answer.

How about we get out while we're young? Well, while you're young.

This truck still has a CD player, and after depositing her back on the passenger seat, I fumble with clumsy fingers through the center console for *Born to Run,* so we can hear somebody who's been there tell us about getting out while we're young, how tramps like us are born to run, about finding out how it feels, and knowing if love is real.

And we do, we get out while we're young, because maybe to be young is to carry whatever shape love takes, away from the leaving and toward a promise.

We cut through the industrial hardscape and into the stops and starts of small beach towns, until the coast highway opens into the last empty stretch before home, and now Bruce is telling me to roll down the window and let the wind blow back my hair, he's telling me we're pulling out of here to win, and not to turn home again, and instead of hearing him, I believe him.

I roll down the window, let the wind blow back my hair, and I'm not turning home again, not yet, I'm taking an abrupt left into the beach parking lot, before the bridge where the nature preserve meets the ocean, with the little yellow puppy's tiny paws bracing against the center console.

The phone screen lights up from the truck's drink holder as I find a space in the back, but this isn't the blocked number of a dead poet, this is a number I know by heart, a number I longed to see for years on my primitive land-line caller ID in Seattle, a number even now, I secretly hope to see.

Her.

Is this some cruel trick by the universe, teasing me away from the pact Bruce and I have made over the last few minutes?

The little yellow puppy swats at my forearm.

The call goes to voicemail.

HEART

The rocks jump from their beds at the water's edge to stub my bare toes, eliciting muttered profane consternation under my breath. I've just set the little yellow puppy's front paws down on the beach when I see him, crawling on his hands and knees, each lunge more careful than the last, across the palm-sized stones leading to the ocean. An empty wheelchair is perched a couple hundred feet away, patiently waiting for the rider's return, but he isn't coming back.

Not yet, anyway.

He's dancing toward the ocean, in spirit and body, and I consider whether he needs, or wants, a hand, but this pilgrimage seems different, rooted in fierce independence and ritual. He pushes himself into child's pose, stretches for a few moments, and lifts himself into a kayak. Flinging his torso to and fro, he inches along the wet sand, until the lapping ocean lifts him into weightless suspension, and a few breaths later he's floating away, paddling with the late afternoon air moving from land to sea, over the waves toward the kelp beds.

Some of us complain about stubbing our bare toes on these rocks, an inevitable part of the landscape.

Some of us cross them with grace and perseverance.

And find ourselves where we belong, a joyous, peaceful trace of spirit, buoyed by a forgiving Pacific and pushed by the first off-shore wind of a dying afternoon.

The little yellow puppy romps through the surf at my feet, alternating between uncertainty and wariness, as the whitewater touches her paws and I trace letters in the sand with my right big toe.

Is.

This.

All.

There.

Is.

A huge bark thunders through my rhetorical question, because yes, this is all there is, and then another bark, but I don't see a big dog anywhere.

Wait.

Up there, on the dry sand.

My breath quickens, my forehead relaxes in joy, and my chin lifts from my chest, as the muscles in my forearm tense and quiver, tense and quiver, and I don't know what's happening, but there are two of me in here, because this is his breath quickening, his forehead relaxing in joy, his chin lifting from his chest, the muscles in his forearm tensing and quivering, tensing and quivering, until my body releases into his and the guy in the gray t-shirt is wrestling with a big brown dog, his jeans plastered to his legs with saltwater, as he tries to keep a small toy away from her.

She's not giving up, burying her nose in every possible hiding place, until he collapses backward and she claims her prize.

A little green plastic fish.

He sure looks happier than he did earlier today.

And a swollen river of remember-whens floods through me, carrying a lifetime in a day to the edge of my own private tidal delta and into the ocean of release, where a melody floating on waves a decade old sings what has been lost.

Heart stops at the door
Where love lives
Love is so beautiful

But heart's been running around
Where the bright lights shine downtown
It's got so heart don't know love no more

And this is what has been lost.

Not time, nor place. Not mother, nor dog.

Not these guides, weaving their own magic into the fabric of this journey.

Heart.

Heart has been lost.

And while my mom has forgotten her past, I've forgotten my present, that I ever wrote this song, this reminder to my heart to find the fire waiting under love's door, whatever she may look like.

So open up love
Love open up the door

The sun touches the horizon, initiating the whitewater exodus of a toddler wearing an oversized Eeyore t-shirt that says *Dreaming of You*. He stumbles into the arms of a man with silvering hair, and they drift toward the parking lot, and maybe an evening of Tator Tots and The Wiggles.

The guy in the gray t-shirt and the big brown dog are laying together up on the beach, her big brown paw on his chest, little green plastic fish still in her mouth. I step through them on my way to finding a place to sit down with the little yellow puppy, now snoring softly in my arms.

My heart pounds a pleading rhythm to the melody pulsing through my veins, as I burrow my lower back into a womb of sand warmed by the afternoon sun, and prop myself up on my elbows to watch the star sink into the sea. I nestle the puppy into my lap and let notes out quietly, allowing my breath to barely carry the song.

Love hears the voice of
Acquaintance
Love is so patient

A little louder, because I want the guy in the gray t-shirt to hear me.

I want to tell him.

Through the door
Heart says

And louder.

I'm sorry for running around
I'm sorry for letting you down
But the lights downtown don't shine so bright
As the fire from under your door tonight

The puppy wakes to turn her head inquisitively toward me.

And now I'm sure the guy in the gray t-shirt can hear me, but he's not raising his head in concern, not stirring, not moving at all, except for the steady rise and fall of his chest, under the protective paw of the big brown dog.

Hello?

So open up love
Love opens up

Can you hear me?

Open up love
Love opens up
Open up love

Can you hear me?

Love opens up the door
And they dance across the floor

I hope he can.

I thank the sky, tinted with orange and red and yellow, for giving me this new little life of pure love, already cracking open the brittle casement around my heart, and let my eyelids flutter in a joyful, emotionally exhausted relief.

Only for a minute.

I'll only close my eyes for a minute.

CHEST

Storm raging on the surface, violence dashing light across the sea floor and onto a chest, sunken in the sand of deep sediment's decay.

Stillness.

Quiet.

Movement.

The little yellow puppy, floating from blue nowhere, now in front of the chest.

Nudging the latch, pushing the lid open.

Small pieces of paper drifting upward in a slow hurricane.

Puppy diving, returning with a Polaroid in her muzzle.

Wrinkling fingers accepting the picture.

Toddler holding a guitar.

Then again.

Small boy in a blue nylon cape.

Then again.

Older boy, in a suit and tie.

Me.

Polaroids pushed into jeans pocket.

Puppy hovering in front of me, suspended in the silence, then gliding toward the chest.

Arms moving like angel wings through fresh fallen snow, following her, flying together, circling the chest, her head lowering to gaze inside.

Almost there, can almost touch her, can almost see the treasure. Buried in old earth of what used to be.

No air. No air.

Must rise. Must rise.

Frantically grabbing for the puppy.

She is falling away, I am rising, she is falling away, I am rising, she is

My eyes fly open in panic at my empty lap. The sun hasn't dropped much further into the sea, but a piercing anxiety is tightening in my chest, creeping up my throat.

I push to my feet and scan the beach, my head on a swivel, until I see tiny paw prints in the hard sand, headed north toward the tidal flat forest.

I run.

Then stop.

There she is.

The big brown dog is nowhere in sight, but the guy in the gray t-shirt is walking straight at me, toward the parking lot, smiling as the little yellow puppy tumbles over his feet. He picks her up and she stares at him as she did me, and now I know what's happening.

My breath does not quicken, my forehead does not collapse in confused frustration, and my chin does not drop to my chest. The muscles in my forearm do not tense and quiver, tense and quiver, because now I know what's happening, what I believed but wasn't sure, there have been two of me in here, a bitter angel and a better one, and I can choose the wings.

He sets the little yellow puppy back on the sand, and she turns to me, whimpering.

She will follow.

Tears pour from my eyes, not of sadness, but of honor for what used to be, tears of resolve for what could be, and I run straight at my bitter angel, exploding through him and into love, joy, and gratitude, the awareness of which is true happiness.

And now the little yellow puppy is running with me in the tidal flat forest, that same backbeat from this morning pulsing against our every step, as dawn's song answers its own question.

But I was not running away

And we rise.

You could say my aim was true

And rise.

Every time I was running

And rise.

I was running to you

Until we're gone, into the cottonwood sunset sky of the nature preserve, like two angels on the wind who were never really here at all.

As a tangled piece of metal, wire and glass waits patiently, screen glowing with a promise of aged apology, explanation, and hope.

Sometimes, waves reform.

GOOD(BYE)BYE

The postal service doesn't deliver to my house. They consider this area rural, which must also mean *inconvenient* in post-speak, because I'm surrounded on all three sides by neighborhoods that do get mail. The fourth side is the ocean, which has no use for real estate mailers, Costco ad supplements, or perfect-family Christmas missives, and regularly regurgitates them back onto the local beach.

So, once a week I head to the post office to check my mailbox. The sole offering yesterday, besides a real estate mailer, Costco ad supplement, and perfect-family Christmas missive, was a kind note from a dad asking me to sign a card for his two-year-old son. He wanted his kid to someday know about the people who had been responsible for some sort of inspiration in his life.

This was a long hoped for, yet unexpected, revelation: I had another fan, besides Emily.

He wrote that an older album of mine, *Saturn Returns*, had meant a lot to him. *Saturn Returns* was recorded in Seattle, where I got my mid-twenties musical feet wet in a rain puddle of musicians much more talented than I was.

I met one of them through an ad I'd placed in the local music magazine. My bass player, who happened to be my childhood best friend, had just quit my band to move to California, and I needed a replacement for what would be my debut full-length album.

The first response I got was from some guy named Joe Bass. I had no idea that he'd played with seminal bands like the Posies, Sunny Day Real Estate, and Sky Cries Mary, but his was the only call I returned.

I'm still not sure why. I'd received a few inquiries, but my tentativeness to proactively connect with others had blossomed impressively by then, even when I was looking for the help and someone else initiated the contact.

He showed up early to my dingy rehearsal space, stuffed in a building shared with a thousand other Seattle bands. Wielding bleach-blonde spiked hair, he sported full-sleeve tattoos needled into him when I was still breast-feeding, and long before it was trendy for uncertain millennials and wannabe bangers to get ink. The word "RENT" ran across the fingers of his fret hand, and either "FOOD" or "BEER" across the other.

I may not remember what those letters were, but I will never forget his first note pounding through the Ampeg 4X10 and punching me in the stomach. For an unfound breath, I was a toddler, back on the family blanket at the local golf course, reeling from an exploding blast in the 4th of July fireworks show.

Except I didn't want my mom to cover my ears anymore.

Joe liked my songs and said I was a gentler soul, which could be challenging in the grunge-hungover Seattle music scene, but he knew some players who might be into what I was doing. He talked to his best friend and former Posies bandmate, who was a drummer off the road from playing with another huge national act. He, in turn, recruited a borderline-legend guitar player new to town.

One of our first shows was opening for a local hero at the Tractor Tavern. Skeptics had reluctantly paid the cover charge and lined the walls with folded arms to decide why these already-famous sidemen had latched on to a decidedly not-hip kid with roots grown anywhere other than the dark, dank, fertile soil of the Pacific Northwest.

My heart was thumping in my throat, but I didn't think anybody could tell, until Joe cornered me in the tiny backstage room and put his gnarled, workman hands on my slight shoulders. I thought he was going to give me a stern talking-to, similar to the one he'd unloaded on our guitar player, who'd shown up slightly hammered to a rehearsal.

Just launch yourself into the room, open up, and show them your heart. I love you, buddy. Nothing happening up there on stage changes that.

So I did. And I gave the band a ton of room to move musically, deferring to them for extended solos, still in awe that they wanted to be on stage with me at all.

The local hero, who was more of a national hero to me since he'd just finished a tour opening for Tom Petty, noticed. He approached me in the same backstage corner as I was putting my guitar back in its case.

Can I give you some advice?

Uh, sure.

You gotta make it about you.

Huh?

I know you respect those players, but they're here to support you… they dig your songs, I can tell. Otherwise, they wouldn't be here, because they don't have to be. So own it.

I walked out of the Tractor Tavern a beer later with a valuable lesson in duality, which would've been life-changing wisdom, had I heeded the message before at least half my life was gone.

Open up and show them your heart. Then own it.

Joe and I recorded two albums and played shows across the country over the next decade. His personal road was rife with cracks in the concrete, potholes, and massive sinkholes, but his reaction was always a smile, a wink, and an offer to help somebody else: one of the purest, truest human beings I'd ever known, with a wide-open heart.

I eventually got knocked out of Seattle by a blindside haymaker, the final bell signaling the end of a lot of special things, including playing music with Joe.

Almost fifteen years passed before I returned to Seattle, on a flight from San Diego. I'd lucked into tickets to see Bruce Springsteen at Key Arena, who unbeknownst to him, had held my hand as I started stumbling toward my music dream.

The almost four-hour show, only a few blocks from where I used to live, galvanized the kind of man I wanted to be, strengthened my faith in humanity, and renewed my drive to leave something beautiful behind when I leave this place.

The next morning, I drove by the studio where we recorded *Saturn Returns*. A boarded-up storefront was all that remained of this magical space, buried in a city I no longer recognized through the massive stakes of steel tech-driven into her heart.

I thought of Joe, and wondered how he was doing. Last I'd talked to him, maybe six months before, he was managing the bar at the Short Stop in LA.

He sounded happy.

The following day, while I was five miles high between Seattle and San Diego, a massive light in this often too-dark room went out.

Joe died.

When I got home from the airport, I opened up the chest under my bedroom window to find my 'Baby's First Book.' Hearing about Joe had lent a visceral awareness to my mortality, and I wanted to set the first of my own story's bookends in place, as if knowing my opening chords might better inform my final coda.

On that exact day, over four decades before, I'd uttered my first words, recorded in my mom's handwriting, when she was still so very much here.

You waved your hand + said bye-bye on 4-3-63

I sat on the floor and tripped through the birth and death and re-birth circle of life, of relationships, of my mom's journey, pushed by the emotional weight of returning to the town and artist that shaped me, where I discovered, twenty years ago, in a room with rain-streaked windows reflecting the woman I loved, that I could use my words and music to affect change in someone.

If I could just open up my heart.

Like Joe did.

Bye-bye, Joe.

Kitt Doucette read this story a few times, crossed some t's and dotted some i's, told me I was writing and living my truth, and disappeared into the great wild of his life's adventure.

I wrote 'What's She Going Home To' with Chuck Cannon, late one night after he played a show at Lestat's in San Diego. I changed everyone else's names, except the well-known artists, because everything actually happened, and the world could use a little less InstaTwitBook stalking.

The photographs are real, and have been returned to the chest under the bedroom window, which from time to time, I still open up.

ABOUT THE AUTHOR

Alex Woodard has toured nationally behind several critically acclaimed albums, earning a few prestigious industry nods while sharing the stage with some of his heroes. His FOR THE SENDER book, album, and concert series has earned praise from Huffington Post (*important, enlightening, and ultimately inspiring*), Deepak Chopra (*a beautiful tribute to the resilience of the human spirit*), Dr. Wayne Dyer (*an inspiring, thought-provoking, and life-changing work*), Ellen DeGeneres (*I. love. this.*), and Billboard Magazine (*one of the year's most touching, unique releases*), among others.

Alex drifts between the California coast and the mountains of Idaho, with a Labrador and two horses, grateful that little yellow puppy finally found him.

Made in the USA
Middletown, DE
16 February 2022